wc 3/65

S0-ALM-538

Discarded by
Williston Park Public Library

Tales from the Wise Men of Israel

TALES *from* THE WISE MEN *of* ISRAEL

BY JUDITH ISH-KISHOR

With an Introduction by
HARRY GOLDEN
and Drawings by
W. T. MARS

VVVVVVVVVVVVVVVVVVVVVVVVVVVVVVVVVVVVVV

J. B. LIPPINCOTT COMPANY

PHILADELPHIA AND NEW YORK

7071
K
Williston Park Public Library

J
398.2
/
1

COPYRIGHT © 1962 BY JUDITH ISH-KISHOR

FIRST EDITION

PRINTED IN THE UNITED STATES OF AMERICA

LIBRARY OF CONGRESS CATALOG CARD NUMBER 62-9345

To

JOSHUA BLOCH

scholar and friend

CONTENTS

Contents

[8]

Contents

PART TWO

In the Years of Dispersion

Contents

Tales from the Wise Men of Israel

INTRODUCTION

NO people—must I say ethnic group?—have developed as high a literary sense of self-mockery as the Jews. While it is true that not all of their literature is of equal excellence, much of what is good concentrates upon the lessons and reforms man learns, or does not learn, from folly, pride, lust, or stubbornness. The Jews have mocked their long, cruel history: they have mocked their accomplishments; and mocked their own sense of purpose. They have done this because they are *chosen* and the way for a people to perform God's chosen tasks is with the proper humility.

This is not to insist all Jews are humble. Indeed not, sadly enough. But humility is something Jews in Jewish literature—literature in the religious tradition of Jewish orthodoxy—usually learn.

They learn it by means of parable.

A parable is a story which has for its aim moral instruction. It is the very best way to preach at people. People need preaching; in fact, most people enjoy it. When the congregation coughs and sits restlessly through the Sabbath services, it is not because the sermon attempts to illumine the moral path but more usually because it is dull. But this same congregation will still their leg-crossing and stop clearing their throats at a parable if the parable instructs them.

Thus, Judith Ish-Kishor's book is in the nature of a great sermon. Its parables collect the complexities of the moral life into hard, particular situations and her wit reduces each of these into its essential meaning.

Tales from the Wise Men of Israel has no hard words in it, nor does it have arcane plots. These are simple stories which lend themselves easily to any willingness to participate in the lessons they propose. Miss Ish-Kishor's style is so limpid, her prose so artless, her diction so simple and direct, one cannot help but participate.

In Miss Ish-Kishor's world there live wonderful people—beggars and dopes, misers and superannuated rabbis and others. Specifically, the Archangel of Death, Alexander of Macedon, Hillel, King Solomon and King David, and, of course, God. Though all of them inhabit a bare world, one stripped of its ordinary, everyday detail, their moral discourse flows all the more freely for this sparseness.

It flows with humor and grace. Miss Ish-Kishor's parables are neither grim nor bitter, though this is not to say they are without meaning. Their meaning is discovered through an ever-pervading irony, as in the parable of Rabbi Joshua ben Levi we see that God will not only trust the promise of a man who has never broken his word but fear that promise as well.

A parable is fit for human consumption, as health experts say, only when both young and old can read it with profit and enjoyment. It is true that the young and old learn on different levels—the young on literal level, the old on the figurative. For both young and old Miss Ish-Kishor has prepared a gift, one wrought with great love.

HARRY GOLDEN

Charlotte, North Carolina

PART ONE

From Talmudic Sources

King Solomon's Ring

THE WISE KING SET HIS SERVANT A
HOPELESS TASK, AND WHAT CAME OF IT.

OF all King Solomon's servants, the bravest and most faithful was Benaiah, the captain of the guard. He had been the King's companion in the fabulous adventures of his earlier days and more than once had saved his master's life. He had never failed in any task that Solomon had set him.

This, indeed, was his only boast; for Benaiah was a man of action, not fond of talking. When he was not on duty guarding the King, he would sit among the courtiers so silent that they made the mistake of thinking him dull. They would tease him; but Benaiah, sure of his place with the King, paid no attention to them.

Once, however, Solomon himself took part in a mischievous trick they were playing on his faithful follower.

"Benaiah," he said one Sabbath evening early in spring, "you are fond of saying that you have never failed in any task for me."

Benaiah bowed respectfully. "That is my only boast, O King."

"Then let me put you to one more test. I want you to find me a certain wonderful ring, so that I can wear it at the Succoth festival. That will give you six months for the search."

"If the ring exists under Heaven, my lord, you shall have it! But tell me, I pray, what makes it so precious?"

"It has magic powers," said the King. "If a happy man looks at it, he at once becomes downcast and gloomy; but if a person in misery or mourning beholds it, hope rises in his heart and he is comforted." Now King Solomon knew that there was no such ring. But he met Benaiah's eager gaze with a smile of encouragement.

"You shall wear it at the Succoth feast," Benaiah exclaimed, "if there be any strength left in me!"

He could hardly wait for the Sabbath to be over, so that he could start on his quest.

First he went to the finest jewelers and goldsmiths and silversmiths in Jerusalem, for he didn't know whether the ring was of silver or gold, set with precious stones or plain. To each man he described its magic qualities, but no one knew anything about it. They had not even heard of such a ring. Benaiah also tried the smaller shops and less prosperous dealers. Always he met with the same raised eyebrows, the same shake of the head.

Ah, this ring must be treasured in some far-off city, thought Benaiah.

When the great caravans came southward from Babylon and Damascus and Tyre, he was the first to meet them, and he spoke to the traders in precious gems, and said: "I am seeking a ring with this magic quality: When a happy person looks at it, he becomes sad; and when a wretched man beholds it, he ceases to grieve and is comforted. Do you have it? I will pay any price. It is for my lord, King Solomon."

These widely traveled merchants also shook their heads. Each told him, "I regret, Captain, that I have no such ring. It may not even exist, for I have never heard of it. I have other rare jewels that will surely please—"

"Look for this ring, I pray you," said Benaiah firmly. "If you have it for me on your return journey, you may name your own price."

He went to Beersheba in the south, to meet the caravans that came up from the cities of Egypt, and from Yemen, the land of perfumes. He asked the jewel merchants: "Can you find me a ring which has the wonderful power of changing a man's grief to joy when he beholds it? Also, it changes happiness to sorrow at a glance."

"Wonderful, indeed!" they answered, "if such a ring exists. But we have not heard of it."

"It exists," said Benaiah. "My lord, King Solomon wishes for it. You shall have any price you ask if you bring me that ring on your return."

He went down to Jaffa, where the ships came in from

the Great Sea and the Ocean of Darkness, in the west, and the Spice Islands and the Land of Ophir, to the east and south. To each merchant he said, "I seek a magic ring. It makes a mourner forget his grief, when he looks at it; but when a happy man sees it, his heart sinks and there is no joy in him. I will pay a great price for it."

And each one answered him, "I know of no such ring. "You are the first to tell me of it."

"Then seek it, in all lands where you travel. For if you bring it to me on your return, you may ask what you wish in payment."

Benaiah thought, How wise is my lord, the King! He knows the things hidden from other men, even at the ends of the earth!

Meanwhile weeks, then months, went by. It was summer. The caravans returned from the north. None of the merchants brought him the ring, or even any word of where it might be found. The caravans came again from the south. "We would gladly help you," the dealers said, "but in all the cities and the markets where we sought it, we have seen no such ring. Nor have we heard tell of it."

Summer was over. One by one the ships returned from prosperous voyages over calm waters, and each of the sea captains and the merchant-adventurers told Benaiah the same disheartening tale. They had not seen such a ring. No one had heard of it.

The last harvest of the year, and with it the Succoth festival, was approaching. Every time King Solomon saw Benaiah, he would say: "Well, how goes the search,

Benaiah? Have you found the ring?" And when Benaiah shook his head, Solomon said with a pleasant smile, "Search diligently, Benaiah. You will surely find it."

"With God's help!" Benaiah said.

But as the days went by and brought no good news, he began to avoid the places where he might meet the King.

Now it was only a week before Succoth. There was no more hope in Benaiah's heart. He could not eat and his nights were sleepless. He dreaded the moment when he must tell the King he had failed. He did not mind so much that the clever young courtiers would laugh at him. But he could not bear to have the King's trust in him shaken.

It was the last night before Succoth Eve. Benaiah lay restless on his bed for several hours; then he rose and dressed and walked about the silent city, hardly knowing where he went. He wandered away from the palace, and the fine houses of the courtiers and those who served the King, through the neighborhoods where the plain people lived.

Night faded from the sky and the east brightened with the rosy fire of dawn as Benaiah went downward from street to street, until he reached the bottom of the valley between the two hills on which Jerusalem was built.

Benaiah looked about him. It was a poor street, with small shabby houses. As the sun rose, people in patched and faded garments came out of their dwellings and set about the morning's business.

Benaiah saw a young man spread a mat upon the moss-grown paving-stones in front of his home, and arrange on it some baskets of silver and turquoise trinkets and mother-of-pearl beads such as people without much money could afford.

Shall I ask here? thought Benaiah. What use, when even the most famous travelers have never heard of the ring? —Still, it will only mean another No.

He approached the jeweler. "I want a ring," he said, repeating words that had lost their meaning for him. "A wonderful ring. It has magic powers. When a happy man looks at it, he becomes sad. When a grieving person sees it, he becomes joyful. Do you have it?"

The young man shook his head. "This is a poor little place, O Captain, and we know nothing of such marvels. . . ."

Benaiah walked away.

But meanwhile the jeweler's old grandfather had come out to sit by the doorway in the early sunshine. He beckoned the young man to him and whispered in his ear.

"Wait, Captain!" the jeweler called out, "I think we can serve you." Hardly able to believe his ears, Benaiah turned back.

The young man took from one of the baskets a plain gold ring, such as is used for weddings. With a sharp tool he engraved something on it and laid it in the captain's hand.

Benaiah looked at it, then he laughed aloud. His heart filled with joy. He had not been so happy since the day he had first started the search. "This is the ring!" he cried, and gave the young jeweler all the money in his purse. "Come to the palace and you shall have more," he added, "for I cannot thank you enough."

He hurried back to his house but was too impatient to sleep. However, he kept out of the King's sight, not to betray his happy secret until the right time should come. He bathed and made ready for the festival. Then in his finest holiday attire he took his place at the banquet table.

He enjoyed the feast, for now that his duty was done he could pay attention to such matters as food and drink. He laughed at every joke, and thought kindly of the clever young courtiers.

When the merriment was at its height, King Solomon turned to Benaiah. A hush spread around the table. "Now, my faithful Captain," the King exclaimed mirthfully, "where is the famous ring?" Of course, after he and the courtiers had laughed for a while at Benaiah's simplicity, Solomon meant to tell him that he had not failed, for no such ring existed.

But to Solomon's astonishment, Benaiah cried: "I have it, O King! It is here." And, almost stumbling in his haste to reach the King's side, he placed it on Solomon's hand.

As the King looked at it, the teasing laughter faded from his face. He became silent and thoughtful, for the magic of the ring was working. The jeweler had engraved on it three Hebrew letters, *Gimmel, Zayin, Yud,* standing for the words *Gam Zeh Ya'avor*—"This, too, shall pass." Thus King Solomon was sharply reminded that all his glory, and the beauty and splendor with which he was surrounded, must crumble away into dust, leaving at last nothing but an old memory and a tale that is told.

When he raised his eyes again, they met Benaiah's with a humbled, grateful look. He was ashamed of the trick he had played on his loyal follower.

"Benaiah," he said, "you are not only as faithful, but wiser than I thought you. This is a wonderful gift. I shall wear it on the same finger as my signet." He drew from his hand a ring with a precious ruby. "And you, in return, must wear this ruby, so that all men may know you as the King's friend."

The Man
Who Didn't Die

WV VVVVVVVVVVVVVVVVVVVVVVVVVVVVVVV

ONE PERSON BROKE THROUGH THE RULES
OF EXISTENCE. WHY HE SUCCEEDED.

R ABBI JOSHUA BEN LEVI was a very pious
man. He spent his days and part of his nights in praying
and studying the holy books. When he gave to charity or
helped persons in need, he did it in secret and not for
the sake of thanks or praise. Withal, he was so pleasant
and friendly that his neighbors loved him no less than
they revered him.

As he grew older he began to prepare for the end of
his life. The thought of Paradise crossed his mind, and he
felt a deep desire to see the home of those wise and brave
spirits who have already left this world. If only he could
win a glimpse of it now!

He prayed to be given a sight of Paradise—merely to
look at it from the outside—before he should come to die.

So great was the favor his goodness had won for him, that God granted his request. One day, an unusual shadow fell across the sacred book Rabbi Joshua was studying. He looked up and saw the Angel of Death.

"God is gracious to you," said the Angel. "I have come to show you Paradise."

Now the Angel thought it poor policy to make an exception in the rules that govern existence, so he had not come in his most benignant aspect. Rabbi Joshua shivered. The sunlight that had warmed him so agreeably before his visitor appeared, took on the chill of ice.

"Am I to go with *you?*" the rabbi faltered.

"I'll admit that, to a human being, I may not seem the most cheerful of companions," said the Angel of Death. "But it is I who lead mortals to Paradise. If you wish to come, you must come with me. However, I shall bring you back. Your time has not yet come to die."

"If that is so," said Rabbi Joshua, eying the shaft of jagged blue lightning in the Angel's hand, "then give me your sword to hold. Else I shall not enjoy the journey."

The Angel had orders to be considerate of Rabbi Joshua's feelings. Reluctantly he gave his terrible sword into human hands; and together they flew through leagues of light and darkness, sunrise and twilight, until the rabbi saw rising from a rainbow a flight of steps and a great arch.

Through the archway they came into a courtyard surrounded on all four sides by walls that stretched upward to the limit of sight. "Here, beyond these walls, is the Garden of Paradise. I can take you no further," the Angel said.

The walls were translucent, water-green. Through them the rabbi saw sweeping outlines, drifts of color, pictures that formed only to dissolve again. It was a sight of glimmering beauty, but he was not satisfied.

"These are marvelous walls," he cried, "but have I come so far to look at walls? I want to see the Garden!"

"Very well," said the Angel, "but I doubt it will be good for you. I shall place you on top of the wall. Look all you wish. Then you must come down."

By lengthening one arm, the Angel lifted Rabbi Joshua to the top of the wall.

Joshua ben Levi gazed upon the garden that human eyes have never seen, amazed and enchanted by its beauty. The loveliest sights of earth were there, but with deeper meanings that he had never quite grasped in life. Loving voices that he remembered from his childhood called to him. Sweet music charmed him then died away into a peaceful stillness that soothed the heart.

Rabbi Joshua felt as though he must laugh and weep, at the same time. Now he understood the Angel's warning; for he loved the beautiful Garden so much, he could not bear the thought of returning to earth. Life there seemed flat and trivial, like a puzzle too easily solved. As if he, the accomplished scholar, should be required to concentrate on the alphabet again.

Rabbi Joshua did an unheard-of thing. Just as he was, alive, and holding the sword of the Angel of Death, he jumped down into Paradise!

"Return!" commanded the Angel, in a voice of rolling thunder. "Give me my sword, or I cannot do my duty! What will be the end of this?"

"I will not return," said Rabbi Joshua.

Meanwhile, throughout the Garden of Paradise, it was felt that a living man had entered. Moreover, into that deathless place, someone had brought the sword of Death. The souls came flocking toward the wall, amazed at this strange happening.

"At least, give me my sword!" groaned the Angel.

"No. For then you will slay me. I will give you the sword only if I may remain alive in Paradise."

"I can make no such promise!" the Angel stormed.

Time was flying. Down on earth, there was a curious muddle in all the affairs of men. Cruel tyrants who should have died a day or two before, were still alive to oppress their people. Sufferers could not expire, nor could innocent souls meet with their reward, for the Angel of Death was not there to release them.

"You know not what you have done!" cried the Angel. In despair he flew away to the throne of God.

"So the man has sworn that he will not give back your sword unless he may remain alive in Paradise?" said the Almighty. "Let us see how he values his word."

The Recording Angel opened his book at ben Levi's record. It showed that in all his life, Rabbi Joshua had never once broken a promise or been false to his word.

The veil in front of God's throne sparkled with God's laughter. "Then since he has never broken his word, We too must hold it sacred. He shall have his way. Go, take your sword from him, and let him remain where he is."

Thus, Rabbi Joshua ben Levi, for his unique virtues, found a unique happiness. He alone of all men, since the Prophet Elijah, was received alive into Heaven.

The Desert
Island

A KING WAS THREATENED WITH A DESOLATE, IN-
ESCAPABLE FUTURE. WHAT MEANS DID HE TAKE
TO BRIGHTEN IT?

IN a faraway country there lived a wise and
wealthy man who spent much time with his young son.
Their home was an estate the rambling gardens of which
held everything to make a boy happy and help him de-
velop into a fine young man. Deeper than all other pleas-
antness, however, was the joy of his father's companion-
ship.

One day, when the youth was full-grown, the father
said to him: "You must be wondering, my son, what gift
I plan for your coming of age. Well, it shall be different
from any you have yet enjoyed.

"I have prepared a fine ship, laden with merchandise;
in this you shall go on your travels to distant countries,

where you can exchange the precious things I have stored on board, for the produce of other lands. There is no better way of meeting with adventure and getting to know the world."

The boy's face glowed with excitement and pleasure. "When do we set sail?" he exclaimed.

But the joy died away, leaving him rather pale and astonished as his father replied: "I shall not come with you. It is better that you discover things for yourself and learn to rely on your own judgment. But I shall watch for news of you and look forward to your return."

When the day of departure came the youth went aboard the handsome ship and bravely waved farewell. It passed out of the harbor.

The sea was calm and for many days they made good speed under a breezy, shining sky. Then a harsh wind bore down on them and a violent storm broke out so suddenly that the sails, as the seamen tried to furl them, were whipped from their hands and shredded. The ship staggered between mounting waves. She lost her masts, her rudder. The very boards were riven apart. Barrels of spices and bales of silk tumbled about in the water, and soon everyone on board was struggling in the sea.

One by one the swimmers were engulfed, all except the young master. He was able to keep afloat, until a great wave lifted him, swept him to the nearest shore, and left him.

When he came to, he had little time to grieve over the loss of his ship and his companions. For he saw a large, gay company of people, evidently inhabitants of the country, hastening towards him. Their approach made him conscious that he was bruised and tired, and that the waves had stripped him of his clothing.

The newcomers welcomed him with open arms, singing in a strange language, and crowding about him with cries of joy. They put soothing ointment on his bruises, rubbed his chilled limbs with oil and dressed him in warm, dry garments. In a chariot drawn by white horses with silver harness, he was driven to a nearby city and to a palace at its center.

As he alighted before the marble stairway and looked up at the lofty entrance, turning again to the cheering crowds, the people near him made him understand that the palace, the city, indeed the whole country, were his, and that he was their king.

The young castaway could not imagine what he had done to earn this good fortune. Everything that he did seemed to please his courtiers and subjects. They praised the diligence with which he studied their language. When he was weary, musicians played sweet music to bring him rest, or else his councilors related the legends and folk tales of the country. He was surrounded by admiration and love.

In return, he tried to be a good king. His efforts, based on what his father had taught him, were more successful than he had hoped. His ministers seemed to approve of him, and his people praised him for justifying their trust.

As he felt easier in his high place, the new ruler was able to think about his own future.

By all indications, this was curiously blank. Other kings had reigned here before him, leaving very little record of their existence. A gourmet's wine cellar recalled the name of one. A pavilion, mournful now in its rusted gilding and soiled statuary, making the very sunlight wistful, had been the favored resort of another ruler. In the venerable library the young King discovered a shelf of books defiantly inquiring into black magic, and a brief diary which had belonged to a predecessor.

What had become of them? Conversation broke off at his casual questions. Even the most vivacious and gossipy courtiers stammered and fell silent. What he saw in their eyes was not so much embarrassment as confusion. They did not know how to answer.

When he tried to find some thread of information by listening to the remarks of his humbler attendants, he succeeded no better. At the mention of a former king's name and a hint as to his fate, their only answer was a wondering sigh, a shake of the head, or a shrug.

He began to fear what he might discover. But resolutely he determined to know the truth.

Among his councilors was one old man with a reputation for profound wisdom. He did not speak often and what he said was not always welcome, but invariably he was listened to with attention. The young King felt that if anyone could enlighten him, here was the man.

One evening, while strolling in the palace garden, the King seated himself near a fountain and retained this councilor beside him while contriving to keep the rest of the court at a distance. They could speak without being overheard.

"Friend," the young King said, "Why have I been so exalted and so honored in this country where I came as a castaway, helpless and alone? What has become of the previous rulers? What is to become of *me*?"

The wise man's eyes were turned upon the speaker, whom he seemed to be studying shrewdly.

"Your reign, sire, is to last one year," he said, "at the end of which you will be placed aboard a vessel and sent away to a desert island—a dreary, isolated spot in the western seas. This was the fate of those who ruled before you. This will be the fate of your successor. Every year we enthrone a new king, who comes to us as you did. We do not know why this is. We only know that such is the course of events in our country.

The young King felt rather than heard a roaring in his ears. His heart thumped, measuring out time. . . . "Could I not hide myself—or escape?" he whispered.

"There has never been an exception," was the answer. But in the sage's tone, the young man detected a fellow-feeling which did not imply pity.

It prompted him to ask: "What would you advise? What can I do?"

The older man relaxed in his seat. "Good!" he said warmly. "I waited for that question. . . .

"You cannot escape the desert island, my King. But you can transform it. Now, while you have the power, send those ahead of you who will make it a pleasant retreat for the later years. Gardeners and builders and farmers. Let them till the soil of the island, and lay it out in fields for the planting of crops, and orchards for fruit, and gardens for flowers and shade. Let them build a house for you. Let them carry to the island books that you love, and musical instruments and paintings and other such objects giving delight to leisure.

"Then you will not fear the fate that awaits you, nor the end of the year."

To his listener, the moonlight seemed to flood the air with silver. Dazzled, the young King closed his eyes.

"I tried to warn your predecessors," the sage concluded sadly. "But they could not always accept the truth. I think you will do better!"

And the young King eagerly set about providing for his future home. Thus it came about that often, during the remainder of the year, when he was tired from the hard work, and dubious decisions, and dangerous crises, he would think of the desert island with pleasure and interest. There he would find rest when he should be freed from his kingdom and its responsibilities. With wonder he awaited the end of his reign.

In this story, say the rabbis, God is the wise and provident father who sends the soul on its journey of mortal existence. The storm represents birth. We are cast up on the shore of life, in which parents, relatives and friends welcome and provide for us until maturity. The year of the King's reign is the span of a human being's life; and the desert island, the dread conclusion—death. But as the King's councilor advised him, it is possible to brighten the unknown future by good deeds, which go before us and transform our portion in the World to Come.

Why Moses Stammered

CLEVER EVEN AS AN INFANT, MOSES HAD
TO BE SAVED FROM HIS OWN INTELLIGENCE.

WHEN God spoke to Moses from the burning bush, summoning him to be his people's deliverer, Moses trembled at his unworthiness.

"How can I speak God's message," he murmured, "either before Pharaoh, or to my people, Israel? O Lord, I am not a man of words, neither heretofore nor since Thou hast spoken unto Thy servant. For I am slow in speech and of a lagging tongue."

Then God answered him: "Who hath made man's mouth? Or who maketh a man dumb, or deaf, or seeing, or blind? Is it not I, the Lord?"

The rabbis explain this passage with a legend from the early days of Moses.

[39]

It is told of him that he was a winning child, lively and precocious. Many a time Pharaoh himself would take him on his lap and play with him.

One day, as the King sat in council surrounded by his advisers, the little boy attracted to the splendid crown of Egypt, reached up and pulled it from the ruler's head.

Silence fell. The councilors, startled by the child's action, realized its ominous significance.

The first to speak said: "Heed the prophecy! It is a warning from the gods. If allowed to live, this boy will bring about the overthrow of Pharaoh and take the crown for himself!"

Among the wise men was the desert sage, Jethro, later to become the father-in-law of Moses. He pleaded: "It is but a child, O Pharaoh! With a child's delight in what pleases the eye. Is there any brighter thing than the crown of Egypt, with the gems of many colors and great size?"

Others agreed there might be no meaning in the act beyond an infant's wonder at the shining crown. But it would be folly, they maintained, to dismiss the matter so lightly.

They devised a test. From Pharaoh's treasury a bowl was filled with jewels. Together with a brazier of burning charcoal, it was set before Moses. The embers outsparkled the gems. If he were a child like any other and merely wanted the brightest thing in sight for a plaything, he would reach for the brazier. If, however, he was gifted with more than natural foresight, he would choose the gems. In that case, he must die.

Now Moses was observant beyond his years. He was attracted to the contents of the brazier. The red coals glowed wonderfully, but their heat troubled him. His eyes half-closed against the smart, his lashes came together.

He turned to the jewels. They were pleasing. Each in its own way. They invited him with twinkles that did not scorch.

He looked back at the bright coals. The wonderful red was pulsing, hot and very bright, then dimmer a little. Hot again. They seemed to him alive. They frightened him. He did not want them.

But the other brightness! He leaned towards the safer sparkle of the many-colored gems, and his hand was opening for the choice.

In that moment God sent an angel to save him. The angel pushed the arm of Moses so that his fingers closed upon a red-hot ember. It burned him, and childlike, in panic, not knowing what to do with it, he brought it to his mouth.

For many days his lips and tongue were swollen. But he was allowed to live, for he had done the unwise thing.

He seemed to be a child like any other.

King David's Peril

HOW THE MEANS MOST DISREGARDED AND DE-
SPISED MAY BE LIFESAVERS IN TIME OF DANGER.

WHEN David was a shepherd tending his father's flocks he had long hours for peaceful meditation. The sheep lay still for the most part, moving only when he led them, or at watering time when he filled the stone trough from the covered well.

In the tranquil hours David would sing to the music of his harp, recount to himself the great deeds of the Judges, or study the beasts and birds of the field.

There were questions that puzzled him. Why did God create flies? he wondered. They stung the tender nostrils of his sheep, they lived on carrion, they pestered and tormented one. Yet each fly in itself is so small that it would never be missed if it had not been created.

Or, Who needs the spider? his thoughts ran on. Its only

[44]

value seems to be that its preys upon flies. Meanwhile, it makes a home in dust and decay, spinning cobwebs in every neglected corner. I doubt if we should be worse off without them.

As he was going home one day, he came upon an idiot. The wretched man dragged his feet as though he had never learned to walk. Instead of words, he uttered queer, broken sounds and pointed to his mouth, so that the young shepherd knew he was hungry. David gave him what food he had left in his scrip, and a drink from the leather water bottle slung at his belt, thinking meanwhile:

Why did the All-Merciful make this poor fellow? Surely, it is worse than death to exist in this manner. To be made in the human form yet without the intelligence of a human being! To be looked upon only with pity or contempt!

Not until many years later did answers reveal themselves to the mind of David.

He was now the people's hero, for he had slain Goliath and won victories in battle against the Philistines. He was favored by the Prophet Samuel, was married to the King's daughter, and had won the devoted friendship of Jonathan, the King's son.

With all this, he was a hunted fugitive. King Saul in desperate envy at the loss of God's favor, was bent on destroying David, and led an expedition in search of him.

One night, when the camp of Israel was utterly quiet, and even the watchers slept, David stole noiselessly through the ranks to the side of the King himself. He took the King's spear and the pitcher of water from beside his head, for he wished Saul to know that he, David—whom he called traitor—had been there, and spared him.

As David turned to go, Abner, the King's general, moved in his sleep and laid one leg upon David's feet. David dared not move, for the restless slumber of Abner might end at any moment. His soul cried to God for help.

A tiny fly came and settled on the general's ankle. Hastily the sleeper moved his leg. David was free.

He escaped to a safe distance from the camp; and shouting, awakened the King and cried to him: "My father, why does the King of Israel fear me? Look for the pitcher beside your head. Look for your spear. And know that I would not harm you!"

Saul was touched, and repented for the moment. But David knew it was the fly that saved him.

As Saul's madness returned and the bitter pursuit went on, David fled to the wilderness of Judea. Among the warped heights and twisting ravines of this desolate region were caves in which he could take refuge. But presently King Saul and his search parties followed him even there.

Once, David actually came in sight. As he fled he heard the King divide his men into separate groups, each to search a nearby section of the hills. Trembling, he crouched in a shallow cavern, one of a series pitting the rocky shelf. He heard his pursuers coming.

"We will search every hole until we unearth him," said the King. "It must be that he is near."

"True," said Abner.

David was trapped. They were only a few feet distant. They halted in front of his hiding place.

"Not here," he heard the general say. "Look, my lord. No one has entered here for days." They passed by and soon their voices faded into the distance.

As David's heart resumed its beating, he saw that since his entrance, a spider had woven its web completely across the mouth of the cave. Its very fragility had shielded him.

There came a time when no hiding place remained for David, in his own land. He was forced to seek shelter among the enemies of his people, the Philistines.

It was not long before David felt that he had been recognized. Only one recourse was left to the Hebrew champion.

David neglected his person. He let his hair fall in tangles over his eyes. He assumed an awkward, stumbling gait. His mouth hung open, allowing spittle to drip on his beard; and he scribbled on doorposts. As he put on the guise of idiocy, no one could have seen in him the handsome, gifted David.

But there were some eager patriots who brought him before Akhish, King of Gath. "Is not this he," his captors said, "of whom they sang in Israel:

> Saul has slain his thousands,
> But David his ten-thousands"?

Perhaps in pity for a ruined enemy; perhaps because idiocy was considered a visitation from the gods, and the person thus afflicted under divine protection, Akhish replied:

"When you see a man that is mad, why do you bring him to me? Do I lack madmen? Shall this fellow remain here, to play the fool in my house? Send him away!"

Thus David lived to sing, in later years:

> How manifold are Thy works, O Lord!
> In wisdom hast Thou made them all. . . .

Beruriah
and the Treasure

THE COURAGEOUS WIFE OF RABBI MEIR, AND HER
HELP IN ONE OF THE HARDEST SITUATIONS THAT
PARENTS CAN KNOW.

B ERURIAH, the wife of Rabbi Meir, is remembered as a fitting companion to her illustrious husband. This story tells of her exceptional wisdom and kindness.

One Sabbath, while Rabbi Meir was at the yeshiva, it happened that their two brilliant young sons fell ill of a sudden fever and, in spite of all that their mother and the physician could do for them, they died.

Beruriah remained alone with them, her mind echoing to the thunderclap of her loss. Gradually she came to an understanding of what she must do. This is the Sabbath, she recalled. God has visited us with His decree on the holy day. It cannot be a matter for grief. I will not profane the Sabbath. I may not weep.

Calmly and tenderly she laid out the bodies of her sons in their own room, covering them with a white cloth.

Then she returned to the other part of the house. She put on her Sabbath clothes and watched for her husband's return. She went to meet him, as usual, greeting him pleasantly, with no sign of grief. They entered the house together and he recounted to her the high points in the discussion at the yeshiva.

When the sun set and the sky grew dusky, Beruriah brought the wine and the winecup, the lamp-wick and the spice box for the celebration of *Havdalah*. Filling the goblet, Meir pronounced the blessing that separated the day of rest from the working week. The Sabbath was over.

Beruriah set out the evening meal. Her husband washed his hands. "Our sons," he said as they sat down to eat. "Have they not yet returned?"

"You will see them soon," she said, and led the talk to other subjects.

"Rabbi," said Beruriah, when they had finished the meal. "I want you to advise me in a difficult matter. Some time ago a stranger passed through the city, a merchant from far away. He bore with him some precious jewels that he had acquired in the course of his journey. But he had still further to go, through a region beset by robbers, and did not wish to risk his gems. So he came to our house, knowing that he could trust you, and gave me the most valuable of the jewels to keep for him until he should pass this way again. Recently he arrived to claim them. But I myself have come to prize the treasures. Must I return them?"

"I am surprised that you question it, Beruriah!" he replied. "You, who are a woman of such fine understanding and high spirit. You know the answer. We must not only return the jewels to their rightful owner, but return them cheerfully. For he honored us by leaving them in your care. We must show ourselves worthy."

"That is what I wished to hear," said Beruriah softly. "Now, dear husband, remember your own words."

She took his hand and led him to the room where the boys lay. When she drew the cover from them, Meir stood for a moment in unearthly silence. Then with a bitter groan, he flung himself down beside the bodies.

"O my sons, my sons!" he cried. "You who were my hope and my pride!"

Beruriah was weeping now, but at sight of Meir's despairing grief she set herself to comfort him. "We should not begrudge their return," she said. "Their time here has ended. Now that God has sent for them, we must let them go in peace, and cheerfully, as you yourself required of me."

Thus she soothed him with wise and tender words until he, too, felt the relief of tears. They accepted the will of God and went on with their lives in courage and patience.

King Solomon
and
the Boastful
Swallow

"WE MALES MUST STICK TOGETHER," ARGUED THE BIRD. AND SOLOMON AGREED.

IN a garden of the royal palace, one day, King Solomon and his queen were enjoying the cool shade and fragrant air. Presently the Queen saw him turn his head sharply and raise his eyebrows, for no reason that she could perceive. Knowing the strange and wonderful ideas that passed through his mind, she asked what had disturbed him.

He replied: "I have just heard a little bird utter an amazing boast. Do you see the two swallows on the edge of the roof? One of them is saying: 'There sits King Solomon, who knows the language of birds and beasts, whom even the genii and demons fear. Yet if I were only to stamp my right foot and sound a particular note, this palace would break into flames, and everyone in it, and all its treasures would be destroyed!' "

"What insolence!" the Queen exclaimed. "My lord, will you not order your servants to catch that presumptuous little creature? It should be punished for its rudeness."

"I should like to know why a bird would say such a foolish thing," said the King reflectively. He gave orders for the royal fowlers and keepers of wild beasts to spread a net over the roof of the palace; and in its meshes the little boaster was caught.

He was brought as a prisoner before the King.

"Well," said Solomon, "are you prepared to stamp your right foot and utter the peculiar note that will make my palace burst into flames?"

"O Solomon, wisest of kings," pleaded the bird, fluttering in its agitation, "I did not mean to say that! No, I will be truthful. I did not mean you to *hear* me say that—"

"Then why say it?" asked the King, with a serious air.

"Send out the fowlers and attendants from before you, O King. Then I will confess. But I pray you, send all these people away."

Solomon nodded gravely. At a wave of his hand, the guards and beast-keepers withdrew beyond hearing distance.

"Now I will tell you," said the bird. "Do you see the other swallow, the one I was speaking with? The graceful bird, with the proudly lifted head?" The King nodded understandingly. "I have just won her for my mate. You know, a man wants to look important in the eyes of his wife."

Solomon burst into a royal laugh. "There is no need to explain further, neighbor!" he said. "But in future, tell your wonderful stories where I cannot hear them. That is all. You are free."

The swallow sped out of the silken net and gladly circled the sky. Then it settled on the roof again.

The King and Queen, still smiling, relaxed once more in the garden stillness. Then the King heard:

"O my lord, you are safe! I was so frightened for you!"

"You feared for *me?* Little silly!" the male bird said. "There was no need to be afraid! The King sent for me only to plead that I should not destroy his palace and burn his treasures. He was ready to give me anything I wished. But I am not greedy. What I do, I do for my own reasons, undeterred by gifts and bribes. That was my reply to Solomon.

"But, truth to tell, and everything considered, he is no enemy of mine. And the beautiful Queen wept and trembled and looked at me imploringly. I could not help thinking what I should feel if *you* were in trouble! So I decided to spare the palace.

"But if only I were to stamp my right foot and whistle that note . . . !"

"Don't do it, beloved!" pleaded the smaller bird. "For I love you because you are merciful, as well as strong!"

"Well, I shall spare them," the male bird agreed. "King Solomon is not a bad king, after all."

[54]

The Body
and the Soul

WHEN a man dies, we are told, he must appear before the Judgment Seat of God. It is then that the deeds and misdeeds of his life are summed up.

Satan—the Accuser, the Hindrance—is there. He gloats over the many sins. But the Recording Angel, while averring these, also gives an account of the individual's good behavior, and his generous, kindly acts.

The divine Judge waits for the soul to speak in his own defense. Perhaps his plea is this:

"I did sin while on earth, Lord. For the body weighed me down. My body's fear of hunger and poverty led me to cheat and to deprive others in order to make myself secure. Covetousness led me on to unmanageable lust and adultery. All this I regret and repudiate. I am free, now,

[57]

of my encumbrance. My soul bows down before the Lord. Will He punish me for the sins of my body?"

In that case, say the rabbis, God may reply with the following story:

"A certain king had an orchard of which he was very proud. The trees were each the finest of its kind. They gave refreshing shade and were loaded, in season, with the most perfect and delicious fruit in the world. He valued this garden above all his other possessions. Often, when wearied from the business of ruling his kingdom, he would retire to the orchard and find rest for an hour in the kind shadow of the trees.

"But he had one great trouble with it. The exquisiteness of the fruit was a temptation to thieves. They would clamber in and not only rob the orchard but break the branches and litter the grass.

"The King built a higher wall around his orchard, but the pilferers climbed this one, too.

"I shall have to place a watchman here each night, he thought; and so he did. But he soon discovered, each morning, that fruit was still being stolen and one tree or another was injured and stripped. The watchman himself was stealing and disposing of the fruit he was paid to guard.

"The King discharged one man after another. Each new guard, after a few nights of honesty, was finally overcome by the lure of the feast that hung just within his reach.

"One day the King hit upon a new idea. He set *two* men to guard the orchard. One was blind, and the other lame. My trees will be safe now, he thought. For the blind man cannot see what he is put to guard, and the lame man cannot reach it. But together they can raise an alarm outside against thieves.

"That night in the garden, the blind man said to his partner: 'Here, you, lame fellow, what do you see of such worth that it must be guarded so trickily?'

" 'Ah!' groaned the other, 'such beautiful fruit! No wonder the King takes so much care of it! I pity you, that you can't see the large golden oranges. And those purple plums, ripe enough to melt at a touch, and such exquisite peaches! Not to mention apples. They're as large as small melons, and they're all colors—red and yellow and green. How I wish they didn't belong to the King. Then I'd really be tempted by them. In fact, it's a good thing I can't walk. Let's not talk about it!'

" 'Good advice,' said the blind man. 'After all, the King has more faith in us than in ordinary men. We are wise through misfortune.' But after a short silence, he went on: 'Still, there's no harm in praising a beautiful sight. You, at least, can see it. I'm missing everything except the fragrance.' And he drew a long breath. 'Tell me, are there any pear trees near?'

" 'Why, you're right, blind man!' his companion exclaimed. 'The tree nearest you is a pear tree.'

" 'I thought I knew that peculiar, delicate scent! What do the pears look like?'

" 'They're golden in color; and when they smell like that, they must be full of juice.'

"Thus they tantalized each other, increasing their eager-

[59]

ness for a taste of the fruit until finally they admitted that only their physical shortcomings held them back from their desire.

" 'I know how we can manage it!' exclaimed the blind man, at length. 'You get up on my shoulders, and tell me which way to walk. You'll be able to reach the fruit and hand it down to me. We shall both have some. Only a taste, you know! For it wouldn't do to be greedy and really rob the king.'

"The blind man carried the lame man among the trees, and the lame man handed down the richest fruit. 'Just a little more,' each one said. And, 'Only the very ripest, that would spoil if we left it.'

"That morning the King found his orchard in as bad a state as ever.

" 'Why blame us?' the blind man argued. 'Can I see the fruit, to reach it? And can the lame man walk among the trees?'

" 'No. But do as you did last night! Take the lame man on your shoulders.'

"Trembling at the King's command, the blind man obeyed. 'The sightless carried the lame,' said the King.

"And he punished them both."

The body has not the soul's understanding and the soul has not the body's powers. When a human being sins, say the rabbis, both are guilty.

Traveling
with Elijah

VVVVVVVVVVVVVVVVVVVVVVVVV

A SCHOLAR LEARNS TO LOOK FOR THE TRUTH BEHIND THE FACTS.

IT is known that the Prophet Elijah has never entirely severed his connection with our world. However, no one knows where, or in response to what need, the great Prophet may make his appearance.

A certain learned and pious rabbi desired so fervently that he be allowed to accompany Elijah on one of his earthly journeys, that his wish was granted. When he stepped through his doorway one morning, he was greeted by a tall, fiery-eyed old man in a mantle of skins.

"Peace to you, my son," said the visitant.

Struck with awe, the rabbi bowed low. He stammered the response: "And to you, peace, my master and teacher! What is your will?"

"That you may go with me," said Elijah. "But first you must accept one condition. No matter how strange my actions may seem to you, do not question me. For if I answer, that will be the end of our journey together."

The rabbi promised readily, and they set out.

All that day they journeyed and shortly before sunset they came to a little house near a country road. They were not allowed to pass it by, for the elderly couple living there came out to welcome them as guests.

"Rest here and pass the night with us," said the old farmer, "for there is no other shelter along the road."

The old woman led them inside and hastened to bake fresh cakes for them while her husband poured water and helped them wash off the dust of the journey.

They were served with fresh milk and cream and home-made cheeses—the produce of the little farm's one cow—and with preserved fruit and honey and barley cakes. The meal was a very cheerful one, for their hosts took delight in the conversation of the learned travelers and with beaming eyes, drew them on to speak of things far away from the quiet little dwelling.

At nightfall they gave their one bed to the guests and arranged a sleeping place for themselves on the floor.

When the rabbi awoke, the morning meal was ready and the old woman had prepared food for them to eat on their journey. But as they took their leave with thanks and blessings, the rabbi was deeply troubled. He had overheard, in the morning prayers of Elijah, a request that the cow—the main support of their kind hosts—should die that day. He asked himself, was this a just reward for such hospitality?

[63]

However, he refrained from uttering his doubts. Elijah was striding along contentedly, his cloak fluttering in the morning breeze. The rabbi remembered his promise. He would be silent and trust to his companion's wisdom.

That evening they came to the estate of a very wealthy man. Presenting themselves as scholars in need of shelter for the night, they were greeted briefly by an indifferent host, who turned them over to his steward, who forgot about them. When the house was quiet, an old servant discovered them where they had been left in an anteroom and provided them with food and a place to sleep, complaining meanwhile of the new, proud ways his master had fallen into, and praying that God would not punish the whole family for his ungodly behavior.

In the morning, Elijah made his way to the master of the house and thanked him ceremoniously for his kindness. Then as he and his companion were leaving by a rear corridor, they noticed a carpenter repairing a broken panel in the woodwork. Elijah paused and, exclaiming that he must reward their host for such generous entertainment, he not only undertook to pay for the work, but remained to see it well done.

The rabbi waited beside him, astonished beyond measure at the Prophet's vivid gratitude. What had the careless, self-righteous rich man done to deserve repayment? But again he held his peace, unwilling to break with his fascinating companion.

That day was the eve of the Sabbath. An hour or two before sundown the travelers entered the synagogue of a

little town. They were eagerly welcomed as men of learning. The president of the congregation claimed them as
his Sabbath guests. After the service he took them to his
home where they shared a good supper and spent the night.
On the Sabbath morning in the synagogue, they were
"called up" to the reading of the Torah. The president
insisted they return with him for the noonday meal. All
that day they were honored and feasted.

Our rabbi was the more surprised, therefore, when Elijah
said as he entered the house of study on the morning of
their departure, "May there always be but one president to
your community! And may he deserve your respect and
deference!" Was this poor blessing what their hosts had
earned, after showing themselves so observant of the Law
and all the traditions of hospitality?

His experience of the following Sabbath was disturbing
beyond any he had yet encountered.

They came to a handsome synagogue where a prosperous
community worshiped. Admiring the many-colored mosaics
of the floor, the exquisite curtain before the Torah scrolls,
the perpetual lamp, all of silver, the velvet-covered seats
for the congregation, the rabbi exclaimed: "Here, indeed,
are people who honor the Lord with their substance and
their wealth."

"Admirable," said Elijah.

They found themselves a place towards the rear and
sat unnoticed. At the close of the service, Elijah stood up.
Silence fell, as he asked: "Who will shelter two strangers
for the night?"

Silence again. The members of the congregation regarded him and his travel-stained companion. The congregation melted away. They were left with the *shammas* who, somewhat grudgingly, took them to his home and performed the duties of a host.

On the morning after the Sabbath, Elijah came into the presence of the community heads and thanked them warmly. "You are all worthy to be leaders!" he exclaimed. "May you all achieve greatness as heads of this community! Only thus can your merit be rewarded."

Once more on the road, the rabbi tried to contain his bewilderment. At last he burst forth: "My master, where is the justice in your actions? Even if we must part, I pray you, let me know the reasons for what you have done. Because they were so good to us, the old couple lost their only cow. In the house where we were neglected, you not only paid for a repair but watched over its completion. To the poor congregation that honored us, you said: 'May you have but one president.' To the wealthy heads of the inhospitable community, you said: 'May each of you be president!' How can this be right?"

"My son," said Elijah, "God does not see as a man sees. In the case of the kind old couple, it was destined that the man must lose his faithful wife that day. I came to test their worth, and to see if she might not be spared to him. Through my prayer, it was arranged that the cow should die in her stead.

"As to the wealthy man who had forgotten the kindness of his fathers, I saw that no further good fortune should come his way. If the wall had been properly repaired, from the spot where it was broken, down to the foundation, a buried treasure of antique gold and precious gems would have come to light. Now it will not be discovered until far in the future.

"The righteous congregation I blessed with peace; for where there is only one head, and he deserves to rule, the community will prosper in contentment and brotherly love. But the congregation where many aim to be leaders and have leisure and power to plot against each other, will have few days of peace or satisfaction. It is a punishment they have brought on themselves, not a blessing."

And while the words still rang in his companion's ears, Elijah vanished.

In the Path
of Alexander

THE WORLD CONQUEROR WAS ENRAGED WHEN THE
JEWS DECLINED TO PAY TRIBUTE. HOW A PUNITIVE
EXPEDITION ENDED IN PEACE, THROUGH THE WISDOM
OF JADDUAH.

ALEXANDER of Macedonia was reaching for
the power that later made him master of the world. He
had scattered the huge army of Persia, and Darius III was
retreating before him, leaving Asia Minor in his hands.

Intent on clearing away all opposition before he turned
to pursue Darius, Alexander sent heralds to the island city
of Tyre with a courteous request for a meeting and nego-
tiations. The King and his advisors read the worst possible
meaning into the cordial words. They cruelly murdered
the heralds and threw them into the sea.

It was an evil day for Tyre! The wealthy city that had
for centuries dominated the Mediterranean coast as queen

of sea-roving commerce, came to know a brilliant, unweary-
ing, ruthless enemy.

Alexander first deprived her of her safe isolation. Against
wind, weather and deep sea-currents, grappling engines
and floating fire-ships, he built a mole three-quarters of a
mile in length connecting the mainland with the invulner-
able rock on which Tyre was enthroned. For seven months
the battered city held out against an epic siege, then broke
down in ruin, flame and massacre.

While still occupied with Tyre, Alexander sent messengers to the small commonwealth of Judah, asking the Jews
to send him some auxiliaries and to supply his army with
provisions. The high priest who, with the leading elders,
governed Jerusalem, sent this answer: "I have sworn an
oath to the Great King—to Darius—not to bear arms
against him."

Alexander replied in anger that he would shortly make
it clear to all men, *who* was able to command their
allegiance. From Tyre he marched down the coast to Gaza,
which resisted him vainly for two months.

He was now on his way to Jerusalem.

The feeling in the city was close to panic. People
thronged the courts of the Temple, crying out their dread.
Jadduah, the high priest, quieted them. "We have done no
wrong," he said. "Our lives and our city are in God's
hands. Let us spend these hours praying for help and guidance."

Within the sanctuary, Jadduah prayed all that day. In
the night he had a heartening dream; and at dawn he put

on the ceremonial robes of blue and purple and scarlet, and the tiara on the golden headband of which "Holy to the Lord" was graven. To the elders he said serenely, "We will go to meet Alexander. I shall lead you. All who wish may follow us."

Wearing their holiday garments of white and carrying flowers and green branches in token of peace, the citizens formed a great procession and followed their elders. They came to a place called Sepha, which commanded a view of Jerusalem and of its approaches. Here they waited. Jadduah stood alone, in the forefront.

A brazen outcry of trumpets shook their hearts with warning. Marching feet and hoofbeats grew louder and nearer. They saw the ranks of an alien army forming on their familiar tawny-golden hills. A group of generals in glittering crested helmets rode forward, and at their head, Alexander.

He drew rein at sight of the waiting throng. The army halted. Then, his eyes dwelling on the still figure of Jadduah, Alexander did a surprising thing. He dismounted and stepping forward a few paces, bent his head and raised his hands in the gesture of reverence.

Cries and questions arose from the ranks behind him. The general, Parmenio, leaped from his horse and came to Alexander. "It is not fitting that you, whom all revere as the King, should bow your head before this old Jew!"

"It is not to him that I pay homage," Alexander murmured, "but to the God who has honored him with the office of high priest. Do you know, Parmenio, that it was

this venerable person, thus attired, who appeared in my dreams while we were encamped at Dios in Macedonia? I was considering how I might obtain dominion over Asia, when this old man exhorted me to make no delay, but boldly to pass over the sea, and he would conduct my army and give me victory over the Persians. How can I doubt that he came from God?"

Alexander went forward, offering his right hand. Jadduah took it.

"Let it not vex the King that we would not help him against Darius," said Jadduah. "Rather, it should stand in our favor. For as we respected our oath to Darius, so we shall be loyal to you."

With one voice the people shouted, "Hail, Alexander!"

He went with them into the Temple courts. There, at his own request, and instructed at every point by the high priest, he offered sacrifice on the great altar.

It was a time of feasting and gratitude. Alexander was pleased with everything he saw. He asked Jadduah if there were some way in which he could show consideration of the people.

"Every seventh year," said Jadduah, "we are required by our Torah to let our fields lie fallow, so that the earth may renew its fertility. During that year we gather no harvest, except from what grows of itself. If it please the King to remit our taxes for the seventh year, it would be regarded by the people as a great benefit."

"It shall be so," said Alexander. "And to commemorate my visit to Jerusalem, you shall have a statue of me, in gold, to stand in the Temple court."

Here was a difficult moment. How to decline the unacceptable gift of a graven image without offense to Alexander, or rebuke to his gracious intent? Jadduah paused and reflected. "We are not permitted," he said at length, "to have any image inspiring homage. As you have witnessed, our God Himself has no image.

"But I have a better way of commemorating the King's visit. Every boy born in this year shall be named Alexander. And as it is our custom to name the newborn after the souls that have departed, Alexander's fame shall flourish among us through all our generations!"

From Behind the Dark Mountains

WHAT ALEXANDER FOUND AT THE END OF HIS ROAD.

IT is known that Alexander was never satisfied with his conquests but wandered everywhere, seeking power and knowledge. The rabbis tell of a strange journey, unrecorded in history, for which they aided his preparations.

First, however, he wished to make trial of their wisdom in philosophy. He questioned them. "What man may be called rich?" he asked.

"He who rejoices in his lot," was their reply.

"Who may be called a wise man?"

"He who discerns what is about to happen."

"Tell me, now, who is to be regarded as a mighty man?"

"The man who subdues his evil passions."

If, when he put this question, Alexander had looked for praise or commendation, he was downcast. For by their measure all his victories fell short. He had never succeeded in mastering himself.

Here were men who would not flatter, and by whom he might be guided.

"How may one come to the Garden of Eden and the Gates of Paradise," he inquired. "For I shall not be content until I reach the utmost boundary of earth."

"That is a perilous journey," they told him. "You would have to penetrate beyond the Mountains of Darkness, in the north of Africa. No man from this side has ever returned."

"Nevertheless, I shall attempt it," said Alexander. "How might it be done?"

"You must go on foot. Load your provisions upon mules which are accustomed to travel in darkness. And stretch cords along either side of your road, that you may be able, should you wish it, to find the way back."

Alexander followed their advice and, after many dark days and nights, he came through a mountain pass into a clean, airy land, largely uninhabited. At length he saw a city rising from a high mound. It was well fortified and guarded. The shields and javelins and helmets of the sentinels glinted in the sun.

Eager for a fight, Alexander ordered the trumpets to sound and sent a herald before him to the city gates.

"Alexander of Macedonia approaches," the herald proclaimed. "What city is this?"

The sentinels on the gate tower seemed astonished rather than startled. They whispered together for a moment then one replied: "This is Kartagena." It was a woman's voice!

" 'Karta-gena'—'City of Women'!" Alexander exclaimed.

He rode up quickly and demanded: "Let me speak with your ruler."

Presently a tall, crowned figure appeared on the tower battlements and spoke with dignified assurance. "Hail, Alexander! Do you come in peace?" Again, it was the voice of a woman.

"In peace, if the city surrenders. Else send your men to fight us!"

"We have no men. But we can defend our city. It is better that you do not test our powers!" The ruler's musical voice vibrated with warning.

Alexander marveled. He had come to the fabulous land of the Amazons!

"Are you invincible, then?" he asked. "Do you challenge us?"

"Would it add to your fame?" she countered. "If you win, it will be said: 'He fought against women.' If *we* succeed, they will say, 'He was beaten by women.'"

"Then it shall be peace," Alexander replied.

The Amazons opened their gates, admitting the whole expedition. They were treated hospitably, entertained and supplied with fresh provisions.

Departing, Alexander said to the Queen, "It may well be said, henceforward, 'Alexander learned wisdom from women.'"

Next he came to a land of rich plantations and pleasant rivers. All the people here were black. They showed no fear at seeing this troop of armed strangers but left their work in the fields to walk alongside the newcomers and bring them to the palace of the King.

The King, a handsome person with bands of gold on his arms, received them affably and ordered a feast in their honor.

The banquet hall was gaily wreathed with flowers and garlands, and the tables loaded with appetizing food. But when Alexander took his seat at the King's right hand, he found before him a golden loaf, and a fish exquisitely modeled in gold. A bowl of golden grapes and figs stood near him, and his goblet was filled to the brim with quicksilver!

The King began on his own food and all the guests began to eat. Alexander gazed at the golden viands set before him, then looked at his host with a questioning smile.

The African King smiled, too. "We felt that we must offer Alexander something extraordinary, by way of a meal. Has he come so far to eat common food? Fruit from the trees, and wine from grapes and bread made of flour, he could have had without stirring from his own country."

The King had the golden dishes removed and real food and wine set before his guest, which Alexander ate and drank heartily, wondering the while, at this barbarian's sagacity.

Curious to see how the King ruled his people, Alexander was invited to sit beside him in the Hall of Judgment. The first case was called. Two men were led in and told to state their complaint.

The first one said: "I bought a piece of land from this man; but when I began to dig in it, I found a treasure of gems and golden ornaments. I brought them to him but he refuses to take them."

"Why should I take the treasure?" the second man interposed. "It belongs to my neighbor. He paid me for the land, and whatever he finds in it must remain his. Is not that the law?"

"I paid for the land," the first man insisted. "That is all I wanted of you. O King—" he turned to the monarch. "I wanted to plant fruit trees. I paid the money one pays for an orchard. Nothing more. How can I keep this treasure as mine?"

Alexander stared in amazement, from one man to the

other, and from them to the King. The King nodded. "You are both right," he said. "Now to resolve the dispute . . ." He thought for a moment then, turning to the first man, he asked: "Have you any grown children?"

"Yes, your Majesty. I have a son nearing manhood."

"And what of your neighbor?" The King turned to the second man.

"I have a young daughter."

"Here we have the solution," the King said. "Let the two young people marry, and the treasure shall be theirs, to start them in life!"

The two disputants were satisfied. They embraced each other, and everybody present applauded the wisdom of the King. Alexander remained silent, shaking his head in astonishment. "How would you judge such a case in your country?" the King inquired of him.

"In my country there would be no such case," said Alexander. "The man who discovered the treasure would hide it and try to keep it for himself. The man who sold him the land would demand the treasure as his and would accuse the buyer in court. Then the King would have both men cast into prison, or slain, and would take the treasure as the property of the crown. That is how the case would be judged."

The King regarded him curiously. "Do you have harvests in your country," he asked.

"Yes. It is a fertile land."

"Does the sun shine? And the rain water the soil?"

"Yes. We have all that the fields need to yield their fruit."

"Perhaps you have animals, or birds nesting in the trees, or bees and butterflies in your gardens?"

"We have, indeed" said Alexander.

"That accounts for it," remarked the African King. "For the sake of the harmless cattle and the innocent birds and insects, Heaven gives you sunshine and rain. If they were not with you, I fear your land would be accursed as it deserves to be—from what you tell me of the dealings of its men."

After many days of uneventful travel from the land of the gentle black people, Alexander and his followers encamped beside a stream. It was cool, and sprightly in sound, and very welcome after long hours of wandering. However, there was nothing else to make it remarkable until Alexander dipped his ration of salt fish in the water. Immediately, the dry morsel became fresh and tender. The stream sent up a stimulating fragrance.

From shouts among his companions, bathing in the stream, Alexander heard about old stiffnesses relieved, and old scars disappearing as though they had never been.

"This river must be one of those flowing from the Garden of Eden," Alexander asserted. "We are near our goal. Let us follow the stream to its source."

They had not gone far before the lively little river lost itself, one could hardly tell how. Against the horizon Alexander saw a cloudy wall, and a gate that was visible only where the light caught its fragile angles.

Alone, he went up to the entrance. "Open the gate to me!" he shouted. To his own ears his voice sounded faint.

"This is the Gate of the Lord, the King of Glory!" came a voice that filled the heavens.

"I, too, am a king!" cried Alexander. "Let me in!"

Silence. Then a resounding answer: "Only the just may enter here."

Alexander pressed against the barely discernible threads of the gate, but they resisted him. He felt weak and overcome. His heart stirred with childish longing. "I am also of some account," he pleaded. "Give me a token, that I may show I have been here!"

Again a pause. An unsubstantial figure within the gate made a curving gesture. Something fell at Alexander's feet. It was a small object that he could enclose in one hand, smooth, with a hollow in its center, and so heavy that it almost weighed him down.

Alexander began the return journey, not knowing whether it was defeat or triumph that he was allowed to return. He brought his token to the rabbis.

They set it on one pan of a scale. In the other Alexander piled gold and jewels; but no matter how rich the treasure, it still swung higher than the solitary small object on the other scale. Indeed, the strange token seemed to become heavier the more one balanced against it.

"Remove the treasure," said a very old man, at length. "This must be the counterpoise." He took between finger and thumb a pinch of soil from the earth and set it on the empty pan.

Gradually, as if with relief at the lightening of its weight, the token swung upward until it was level with the pinch of dust.

"I can answer your question, O King," said the sage. "This is the bone surrounding the eye of man. It is relentless in its curiosity, insatiable in its desire. Only the earth from which it comes can quiet it. Only the grave can give it rest."

An overwhelming sadness clouded the spirit of Alexander. He felt humbled. From his fearless journeying, and his will to force himself upon the attention of supermundane Powers, he had brought back only a symbol that ranked him with the common man and assigned him the common fate!

The Patience
of Hillel

ABOUT THE WISE MAN WHO NEVER LOST HIS TEMPER.

GENTLEST and wisest of the sages was Hillel. Without worldly advantage or ambition, entirely through his mental gifts, his devotion to study and his endearing character, he arrived at such pre-eminence that he was chosen president of the Sanhedrin, the highest religious council in Judea. He was no longer addressed as "Rabbi," or even "Rabban." His name alone was his distinction.

Yet he was simple in his manner of life and easy of access. That was why, when two young men—one a Jew, the other a visitor to Judea—devised a test of his amiability, they had no difficulty in arranging all the details. The foreigner wagered a considerable sum that he could make Hillel angry. The Jew, on his side, wagered that it couldn't be done.

To begin with, they knew that Hillel regarded personal neatness as a necessary virtue. Once, in answer to a comment on his meticulous care of his appearance, he had replied: "Do not the Levites and the many attendants labor to keep the Temple and the Temple courts clean and beautiful? So, too, must we care for the body, in honor of the soul it enshrines."

The two youths decided that the best, because the most trying time for their intrusion on Hillel, would be the hour before sundown, on the eve of the Sabbath.

He was washing his hair and beard when a loud thumping on the door disturbed him. He wiped himself as dry as possible, hastily smoothed his hair, put on his robe and went to greet the visitor.

Two young men—one in foreign attire—stood on the threshold. "I want to speak to Hillel," announced the stranger aggressively.

"I am Hillel," was the low-toned answer. "What is it that troubles you?"

"It has been told me, you are very wise. I want to ask a question."

"Ask," Hillel murmured. "If I can answer, I shall be happy to do so."

"Why is it," demanded the stranger, "that the heads of Babylonians are not well rounded?"

The question was meant to be offensive, for Hillel himself was born in Babylon. "My son, that is a difficult question," said Hillel mildly. "It may be the fault of their midwives who, perhaps, lack skill in shaping the heads of the newborn." Without a word of thanks the visitors turned away and left, slamming the door behind them.

Once again Hillel immersed his head and face in the water. No sooner was he thoroughly wet and disheveled, than the loud hammering broke out again. Again he dried himself, combed his hair and put on his robe. Opening the door, he found the same two intruders.

"Another question weighs on my mind," said the stranger, with a puzzled frown. "Why do the citizens of Palmyra have bloodshot eyes?"

"My son, that is a good question," said Hillel. "Palmyra is situated among rocks and sands. When the hot wind blows from the desert, it carries tiny particles that irritate the eyes and give them the bleared or bloodshot appearance."

The stranger grunted and left as noisily as before, his companion cheerfully abetting him. Hillel renewed his attempts to make ready for the Sabbath. Again they were interrupted by the unwelcome callers.

"While we are here, I want to know what makes the feet of some Africans so broad?" the foreign youth blustered derisively.

"My son, that is a natural question," Hillel responded. "It must be that they live in a marshy district, so that their feet spread, almost as if webbed, in order to walk safely."

His hearers made a boisterous exit.

By this time there was need for haste. Shrugging his shoulders and smiling a little at human caprices, Hillel tried again to finish dressing. For the fourth time the house resounded with a summons to the door. Once more Hillel made himself presentable and appeared.

"I have heard much in praise of your Torah," said the stranger. "I may even wish to become a Jew. But I shall only be here for a short time, and can't be concerned with deep study. So tell me about your Law. Give me the essence of it, if you are able, in the time that I can remain standing on one foot."

"I believe I can," said Hillel, amused. "Take your stand." The young stranger balanced on one foot. "What is hateful to you, don't do to any other person. That is the entire Law," said Hillel. "All the rest is merely commentary."

The questioner stood on two feet again. "So you're the famous Hillel!" he commented glumly.

"That is my name."

"I'm glad there are no others like you, in Israel!"

"Why? What harm have I done you?"

"I made a wager with my companion, here, that I could make you angry. And because of you, I've lost my money—more than I can afford!"

Hillel laughed. "Better that you should lose your money," he said, "than that Hillel should lose his temper!"

When Supper
Was Late

THE WIFE OF HILLEL FOUND HERSELF IN DIFFICUL-
TIES. WHAT THE WISE MAN HAD TO SAY ABOUT IT.

THE wife of Hillel was known to be a charitable woman. Moreover she believed, with him, that one should not separate oneself from the people.

A haggard, frowning individual knocked on her door late one afternoon, and being invited in, spoke of his embarrassment. "I have waited all day, praying that the Lord might send help. But now the time is short. In an hour or two, the matchmaker will be at my house, bringing the parents of him who might be my daughter's bridegroom, if things go well. The young man, too, is coming to see her. You know my Nehamah—how winsome she is, how full of charm!"

Hillel's wife listened with a sympathetic glance, as she moved about the kitchen, busy with the evening meal.

[88]

The girl was, indeed, so lovely that she brightened her poor home, and so engaging that it was a kind of happiness to be near her.

"Why should my child be put to shame?" the troubled father went on, his face reddening. "The matchmaker has told them I am not in good circumstances. But they are wealthy and will take my girl without a dowry, since they have heard so much regarding her own worth.

"Still, there is a degree at which poverty becomes ugly. My house is so bare that I can offer no hospitality. There is nothing to put on the table—no refreshment of any kind to set before the guests.

"Perhaps I deserve my afflictions! But my child—why should *she* be humbled, and her future happiness endangered?"

"Peace! Peace to you, neighbor," said Hillel's wife, calming his misery. "God sent you to me. Here, take what He has provided." And she gathered the entire evening meal, which was now ready upon the hearth, and placed it in a close-lidded earthen vessel. She brought a cruse of wine, a pot of preserves, and the small cakes she had prepared against the coming Sabbath. Packing them in a covered basket, she hurried him to the door, interrupting his tearful thanks. "God's blessing go with you! *Mazzel-tov* to your daughter, and may you live long to enjoy her happiness!"

When she was alone, the rabbi's wife realized that time was short for the cooking of another meal. She had to rebuild the fire, take the grindstones and prepare flour for cakes of bread to be baked again. She had to make another supper from the very beginning.

Returning at his usual time, Hillel found her busy with the cooking. He greeted her, and with no comment, went cheerfully to his books and began to study. Time went by and the cooking odors made him hungrier. He observed, too, that his wife had a hurried, apologetic air.

"My wife," he said presently, "You are always ready with supper when I come home. Perhaps something happened to delay you?"

"Yes, Rabbi," she faltered. "It *was* ready. But I gave it away."

"Ah? Then there was need?"

"Great need. Or so it seemed to me. . . ." And she told him of the father's plight, finishing humbly, "Forgive me, Rabbi, that I failed towards you—"

"Forgive you?" smiled Hillel, coming to her side. "You did exactly right. And I thank God that He gave me such a treasure of goodness in my wife!"

The Three Friends

WHICH OF THEM IS THE REAL "FRIEND IN NEED"?

A certain man had three companions, all of whom he valued, but by no means equally. The first and closest of them had become his chief reliance in any difficulty, whether business or personal. He trusted this friend completely and was happiest in his company.

For the second friend he also felt a warm affection. He cherished their relationship, but did not have quite so much confidence in him, or such need of his presence.

The third friend he took casually, liking him and enjoying his company when there was time and occasion for seeing him.

There came a day when this prosperous, highly respected citizen saw the King's messenger appear before the entrance of his handsome house. "I am to bring you before the King within the next few hours," the herald said. "Make ready to follow me."

It was a terrible shock. The man said to himself: "Surely,

some tale-bearer has lied about me and brought false charges. I need an influential person to speak in my defense. I will bring the good old friend who has never failed me."

He hurried to his dearest friend and spoke of his need, confident that this most faithful comrade would come with him to the King, and plead his cause against any traducer. But to his dismay, the person in whose friendship he had put his trust looked at him coldly and merely shook his head. "This is no concern of mine," he said. "I am unable to come with you."

Broken-hearted, the man turned away. He went now to his second friend, and pleaded for his company and support in the appearance he must make at the King's court.

This one was warmly sympathetic. He wept at his friend's plight, and made ready to accompany him. "I will go with you to the very gate of the King's palace," he promised. "More I cannot do. There is no help for it."

In despair the man made his way to the third friend, whom he had treated lightly. He explained his predicament. "I am guilty of no crime," he said, "yet who knows what false accusations may have preceded me? I am afraid, too, that I may not conduct myself worthily in that august presence—" He broke off, for he remembered the former refusals and felt unable to face another. "What shall I do?" he ended brusquely, turning his eyes away.

The third friend took his hand. "I will go with you," he said calmly. "There is nothing to fear. We shall appear together before our King." And as the man gazed at him in humble gratitude, he went on, smiling: "I can always gain admittance. And believe me, I will plead your cause as though it were my own."

And so it came about. The third companion spoke eloquently in the man's defense and presented such evidence that he was cleared of blame and found favor with the King.

Who was the influential friend? He symbolizes a man's good deeds, that always help to justify him when he comes before God for judgment. The second friend, who truly sympathized but could do no more, represents the family and relatives and friends, who can follow him as far as the grave. While the first, in whom he had placed the greatest reliance stands for money and our earthly possessions, which have no value in the World to Come.

The Generous Physician

GENEROUS EVEN IN THOUGHT WAS ABBA UMANA,
WHO DISARMED CRITICISM BY NOT MAKING USE OF IT.

ABBA UMANA was a physician who had attained great celebrity, so that he was known as Father, or Chief, of the Skillful. His fame was further amplified by tales of his generosity.

For instance, he was most considerate of a patient's pride. He would not name a fee, lest it be more than the sick person could afford. He had a box set up in a private corner of his house, where those who came to him for advice and treatment would deposit whatever they could pay. If without means, they need not be put to shame, while the rich could give genuine proof of their gratitude.

It worked out very well for Abba Umana. He was able to live comfortably; and the report of his magnanimity spread beyond his own land.

It spread to faraway Babylonia, where Abbayé was head of the Talmudic academy. Two of his pupils were sick and seemed to make no progress under the treatment of neighboring physicians. Abbayé sent for them. "You shall go, my sons," he said, "to Abba Umana. Money for the journey will be provided, and for your lodging in the town until, God willing, you be cured. In the meantime, satisfy my curiosity about that saintly man. See if he is really as generous and good as they say."

The students set out. When they came to Abba Umana, he diagnosed their ailment and said: "You must come to me every day for treatment. Meanwhile, as students journeying from so far away, you shouldn't be allowed to waste your money paying for lodgings. Stay in my house and be my guests until you recover. You will be welcome. There's nothing I like better than hearing about travel and foreign lands and different customs."

As for putting money in the box, Abba Umana would not hear of it. "I should pay *you*," he said, "for the pleasure of your company!"

The students spent several days in great comfort at Abba Umana's house. They joined him at meals, while he listened delightedly to their college gossip, and drew them out about their teachers and the government of the community. They shared an excellent room and enjoyed the sights of the city.

In short they felt an increasing unwillingness to make trial of their kind host's generosity. They already knew him as the finest person they had ever met. Still, to obey the request of the fatherly Abbayé, they planned to put their doctor to a test. When he told them they were cured, but asked them to remain with him a day or two longer, they thanked him and assented.

Before dawn on the following morning, without a word or message of farewell, they stole out of the house, taking with them the rich silken tapestry that had covered their bed. They took their stand in the market place at a spot where they knew Abba Umana must pass in his daily routine, and offered the coverlet for sale.

As the physician came up to them, they shamelessly displayed it and asked him what he would pay for it. "Seven gold pieces," said Abba Umana amiably. "At least, that is what I paid for a coverlet very much like it." And to their amazement, he took that sum from his purse and gave it to them.

"But do you not see," exclaimed one of the students, not closing his hand on the gold, "that this is your own property?"

"We stole it from your house," cried the other youth. "Aren't you going to call us thieves—and—and ingrates?"

Abba Umana laughed indulgently. "You must have a good reason for what you are doing. From what I have seen of you, you cannot be thieves. It may be you have a righteous purpose in mind. Perhaps you want to raise money for a special good deed, such, for instance, as buying a Jewish slave or captive in order to release him, and are merely ashamed to say so."

"Our only purpose," they told him, "was to put your generosity and faith in mankind to the test. And we're content. All the praise that has been given you is well deserved!"

"What flattery is this that you pour into an old man's ears!" the physician rejoined. He would not accept the coverlet. "I have enough of such things," he said. "Besides, in my mind I knew you had good intentions and I already devoted it to a charitable purpose. Consequently, it is no longer mine."

"But we have no place for it," the students insisted. "It is far too handsome for our use."

"Sell it, then, and divide the money among the poor."

Abba Umana sighed. "Look about you! There are far too many who need it!"

That was the satisfying story they brought back to Abbayé.

PART TWO

In the Years of Dispersion

Love from the
Dead

A WANDERING SOUL SEEKS JUSTICE FOR THE LIVING.

$\mathbf{A}$T a seacoast town of Asia Minor, a Jewish
traveler walked lingeringly about the harbor.

He was in great distress of mind. Though the affair
that had brought him to this city was by no means settled,
he must soon make ready to embark for home. The time of
harvest was drawing near, when he must return to his
fields and vineyard. Yet how could he leave this place,
without her whom he longed to take with him as his wife?

True, the need for departure was put off by the fact
that no ship sailed this day that could bring him back
to his own country. Avidly, Gabriel ben Joab took the
delay as a good sign, reviving hope. But the hope dwindled
and paled as he considered it. What difference would a
day or two days bring about, in the decision the rabbis had
given, that his beloved—a widow—might not remarry
without eyewitness proof of her husband's death?

Ben Joab's heart ached over the mischances of life. Here was Tsiviah, his childhood love, almost within reach again—but once more withheld from him. Bitterly he recalled the time when her foster-parents had given the lovely young girl, orphaned from birth, in marriage to a relative of theirs—a prosperous merchant by many years older. It was thought that they had done well, securing her future. Amos ben Asher had been a kind husband.

Yet only five years had passed before she was widowed. Amos ben Asher never returned from the voyage in which he had ventured most of his wealth. By this time, the foster-parents were dead. In anxiety and renewed concern for her, ben Joab had come to offer what help she could accept.

He had found her in need, at the edge of a sordid life that might engulf her. Love had revived in him; and Tsiviah's happiness at his coming had welled from her eyes in tears. She had taken her plea to the rabbinical court, and they had rejected it.

Ben Joab's eyes were smarting. He had stared too long at the waters of the harbor, shimmering under the morning sun. He turned aimlessly away from the quayside.

Several times in his random pacings he had come upon a pale youth in disordered clothing who lay heavily asleep amid some bales of merchandise, lost to the waterside noise and bustle. Now, as ben Joab was leaving the harbor, the youth suddenly leaped to his feet, and glaring at him wildly, threw himself upon the traveler as if to detain him.

Ben Joab staggered a little but righted himself. "Haven't

slept it off yet?" he queried, setting the young fellow on his feet. "Come, I'll bring you home. Where is your dwelling?"

But with a resentful cry the young man burst from the grip of his would-be helper and with surprising power lurched away, up one of the sloping streets towards the center of the city. Ben Joab having nothing else to do at the time, and glad, perhaps, of the distraction, followed to see that he came to no harm. He caught up with the youth near a market-place and guided him by force out of the way of camels, laden donkeys and trundling, heavy ox-carts.

Street boys followed with yells and mocking outcries.

Bystanders laughed. A fruit-dealer grimaced in sympathy. "Woe to his parents!" he exclaimed. "Jesse ben Gershom again, the young rogue!"

The traveler divined in him a fellow-Jew. "You know them?" he asked. "Where is their home?"

"There, on the hill." The other waved toward the row of mansions, each set in a walled garden. "Fine people. Well respected. He is their one grief, drinking with wild companions, night and day. It is a *mitzvah* to take him home!"

"Which way shall I go?"

"To the left, by the Street of the Sandalmakers."

Apparently, this was not in keeping with Jesse ben Gershom's wishes. With unnatural force, he strained in a different direction, at the same time uttering a roar of woe that seemed impossible from so slight a frame.

"I have never seen him like *this*," said the fruit-dealer, alarmed. "You need help with him. I will go with you." And he left his booth in charge of an assistant.

The youth seemed driven by an invisible force, outside himself. "Let him go where he will," the traveler suggested, "until his strength be spent. Then we can easily carry him."

Still howling woefully he drew the two men with him out of the market-place, along a crowded thoroughfare, up to a quieter, residential street. He ceased to shout and struggle but drove himself forward swiftly until, on the steps of a synagogue, he dropped and fell instantly asleep.

"What does he want here?" his fellow-citizen exclaimed.

"Let's bring him in," said the traveler. "In a quiet spot the madness may leave him."

Shaking his head, the *shammas* admitted them to a dim anteroom of the house of study; but their troublesome charge did not rest. Instead he awoke and listened intently to the ceaseless hum of voices in the next room. Again, with a movement and utterance too powerful for his size, he sprang up and yelled.

Amid sounds of disturbance the door opened and the students hurried out. The rabbi came, a thin old man with a scanty white beard. "It is ben Gershom," he said. "Let his parents be called." Somebody left with the message.

But, "I have no parents!" the youth burst out, in a deep, gruff voice that seemed to wrench his ribs. "I am alone!—I have no place!—I have nothing!"

"He must be possessed, to speak so!" the caretaker moaned.

"Possessed by a *dybbuk!*" "It is well that he came here!" Murmurs passed among the older men.

"Bring him in," said the rabbi, in his tremulous, silvery voice.

Gabriel ben Joab led the youth, who this time came quite willingly, to a seat near the rabbi's desk.

Clearly the rabbi doubted that he had the power to drive out a wandering spirit so forceful as this. "Help me with your prayers, brethren," he said to those around him: and he himself prayed silently for a time, while Jesse ben Gershom seemed to sleep.

The rabbi was moved to begin. "Dybbuk, what do you seek?" he demanded. "Why are you not at rest?"

The eyes opened with a defiant stare. "Because I sinned. I sinned and have not yet been punished. When I was younger, I committed the sin of adultery. I took the wife of another man." The words were loudly spoken, as if ejected; but the body remained quiescent.

"Who was the woman?"

"I will not tell you. She is long dead, and gone to her rest. But she was of this city. Her children live and are known. Why should I bring shame on them and her?"

"Then your sin troubles you?" The rabbi shook his head. "It is a grievous sin." He sighed.

"I am no worse than other men," the dybbuk announced. "I see two here, who sinned in the same way." The arms jerked forward, each pointing to a student. One of the young men blushed fiery red; the other sat down abruptly, covering his face with his hands. Heavy laughter shook Jesse ben Gershom from head to foot. He seemed to flutter like a rag in the wind.

"This is unseemly, Dybbuk!" the rabbi murmured reproachfully. "You have sinned, and we will join you in penitential prayers. But you trespass again, stealing the body of this boy."

"What else could I do? I was drowned. My body decayed in the ocean. I went into a fish. The fish was caught and brought to market. I escaped into a cow, in the cattlestall nearby. But the cow went mad and had to be killed. Outside the slaughterhouse, I found *him*." Jesse ben Gershom's hand tapped his own bosom. "His soul is in a stupor. It made no effort to resist me. I entered and filled his frame. Too small for me, yet a refuge—a vehicle to bring me here!"

A shudder passed through the listeners.

"What do you seek here, dybbuk? Who are you?"

"Amos ben Asher, of this city."

The traveler sprang to his feet and a cry escaped him. Was this the soul of his rival that spoke? He waited, rigid with contending emotions.

"Have you children?" the rabbi went on.

"None."

"Had you a wife?"

Jesse ben Gershom broke into pitiful sobs and the voice of the dybbuk continued, in quiet, tender speech between the outbursts. "That is my injury! That is my claim against you! My wife, my poor little one. I was lost at sea. My ship sank in a storm, with all its wares. And she, an orphan, without means, without a husband to protect her, has been driven to become a harlot. For she is fair to look upon, and *you* would not grant her permission to remarry!"

"It is a necessary rule that we must observe," said the rabbi. "A woman who has not proof of her husband's death, cannot become the wife of another man. Who knows but her husband may return, and a great wrong be done."

"Then I give you proof!" the dybbuk cried triumphantly. "I tried to reach you by other means." The rabbi now recalled the dreams of storm at sea and sinking ships that had troubled him. One of the *dayanim* realized why, for days, the verses from Psalm 107, beginning:

> They that go down to the sea in ships,
> That do business in great waters . . .

had repeated themselves over and over in his mind.

"Rabbi," he whispered, "the *agunah* who came to us yesterday. Perhaps it is she."

"What do you ask of us, Dybbuk? What will make you leave the body of this youth?"

The dybbuk replied eagerly: "There is one here who knew her when she was a child. Let her be his wife. Allow it!"

Gabriel ben Joab came forward, but he did not feel the ground beneath his feet. His head whirled with a joy too strong for him. He must make sure if this were the truth! He came close to the rabbi and the exhausted youth and said, so that they alone could hear him, "Do you speak of Tsiviah bas Ari?"

There was a resonant shout of assent from the dybbuk. Ben Joab went on, his voice choked with gladness and with gratitude to his rival. "Rabbi, it is the truth he speaks! I will take her with me to the place of our birth. That is all I wish! And it shall be well with her!"

The rabbi and the dayanim conferred for a moment. Under the rabbi's direction, a scribe wrote several lines on a piece of parchment. The rabbi signed it.

It seemed to Gabriel ben Joab that his heart had wings, as he grasped the document and hastened away.

"Now Dybbuk," said the rabbi firmly, "leave the body of this youth. You are doing him injury."

"I ask but a moment more!" the dybbuk pleaded. "It is long since I have heard a good word."

By this time the parents had arrived. The mother wept despairingly. The father's face was gray.

"Begone, Dybbuk! Have pity on his parents!" The rabbi's voice was stern, though it shook with agitation. "Must I invoke the ban against you and drive you from the congregation of Israel?—God forbid!"

"No. I go. But you will read the penitential Psalms for me?"

"And we will mourn for you. Go. And do no harm to the lad."

"I am gone."

A puff of breath from the nostrils, and Jesse ben Gershom was only a preternaturally wearied boy—frightened, ashamed, and sick of his wild companions.

He embraced his parents, and from that day forward, he led an admirable life.

The Prince
and the
White Gazelle

A MEDIEVAL PRINCE THINKS HE IS WISER THAN HIS
KINDLY, TOLERANT FATHER AND SETS OUT TO PROVE IT.

A small German state, at some time during the Middle Ages, was ruled by a wise and beneficent prince. He remained at peace with neighboring rulers, for he had no other ambition than to see his country well governed, with justice and understanding of its people's needs. To this task he devoted his life. The land flourished. The inhabitants were prosperous and content. Even the Jews found a peaceful refuge here, for the Prince would not allow them to be taxed beyond reason, or molested, or victimized in any way. It was even known that a Jewish merchant, Meyer Rothfels, had on occasion been his trusted adviser.

But the good Prince could not live forever. As he felt himself failing in strength he began to give his eldest son charge over the country's affairs. Especially, Prince Gottfried recommended his Jewish counselor, Meyer Rothfels. "When you are not content with the advice of other men, that is the time to send for Rothfels," the old Prince said. "He is deeply sagacious. He will find a way out of your difficulty."

Prince Erhard thanked his father respectfully; but to himself he said: "May I never be so poor in wisdom as to ask advice of a Jew!"

The old Prince died and the young man ruled in his stead. In most respects he did justice to his father's training. The people were pleased with him.

However, there was one change noticed by those whom it concerned. Rothfels was never called to the palace; and one day the Prince declared to his councilors that he would issue a decree giving the Jews of his country one month in which to gather their belongings and prepare for banishment. They would be allowed to remain if they became Christians. The most influential of his advisers agreed in praising Prince Erhard's "wise severity."

On the following morning Meyer Rothfels, who seemed to know about every contingency before it arose, gained admission to the Prince's chambers. Erhard had just awakened. As his attendant helped him dress, he listened unconcernedly to the old man's pleadings that the decree should not be made public—that there be further consideration of the possible results to the country's well-being

—that the young Prince should remember his father's friendship to a hunted people. . . .

"All this we have considered," said the Prince. "It pleased my father to indulge you. Under God, I shall be a stricter friend. The decree stands."

Leaving the old man red-eyed and shuddering, Prince Erhard strode into the morning room. He began on his breakfast, which was served before a window opening on the park of the palace grounds. As he ate, there crossed his line of vision a white gazelle, limping as though it were hurt. What a lovely little creature! he thought. Wounded, too. I can easily catch it.

He rose from the table and taking the bow and quiverful of arrows from a man-at-arms on guard, he leaped over the low windowsill into the park. As if the gazelle knew of his coming, she quickened her pace a little, but could not go fast enough to escape him. Feeling sure of her, he followed in leisurely fashion. Near the fence separating the park from the forest, she seemed to gather her strength. She leaped across the paling and spurted up a narrow path between the fir trees.

The Prince set an arrow to the bow and drew the string. But before he could let fly, the little creature turned its head and gazed at him. The big brown eyes shone with a human entreaty. They were full of tears.

He lowered the arrow. "I could as soon slay a beautiful woman," he murmured. "No, I shall take it alive. It will be pleasant to keep it as a pet." He opened the gate and quickened his pace. The gazelle began to run, too. It led him a long chase, farther and farther into the forest.

He flung himself down, panting. Then the pretty creature came near and lingered so close that he could almost reach up and put an arm around her neck. When he made the attempt, however, she moved off, just beyond him, and he started after her again.

So it went the entire day. The Prince was so absorbed in the chase, and always so near winning, that he could not give up.

All at once he realized that the sun was setting. A last red ray lit up the forest path. At the same moment, the white gazelle sprang into a thicket and disappeared. Cursing with rage, the Prince scrambled after her but succeeded only in losing the cleared pathway.

Before nightfall he found some nuts and berries that somewhat satisfied his hunger; and since he had left the palace without a cloak, he was obliged to burrow among the dead leaves for cover against the chill of autumn.

By the first light of morning he tried to retrace his steps. But he could find no landmark. Though he had often gone hunting among these oaks and hemlocks, he had been attended by experienced foresters and had not troubled himself to learn his way about. The thought that by this time his followers would be searching for him, gave him hope. But he walked all that day without sight or sound of a human being. On the following day he set out in the opposite direction, with no better success.

For sixty days the Prince wandered about in the forest.

His velvet doublet was muddy and full of holes. His hose had long ago been torn to shreds by thorns and briars. His shoes were broken and let in the rain. He was bearded now, and his hair was long and ragged.

Apart from his present plight, the thought of what must be happening at the palace tormented him with anxiety and useless speculations. What were his ministers doing? What did his people think? Did they give him up for dead?

One day the snow began to fall, whitening all the forest. The Prince looked up at a strip of gray sky and despair overwhelmed him. His time had come. He would surely freeze, ill-clad and shivering as he was.

The deep silence was broken by the sound of cracking branches as some creature pushed its way through the underbrush. The Prince turned his weather-stained face with little expectation of good. But it was not an animal that approached.

The Prince saw before him a charcoal-burner—a big, rough man, warmly dressed except for his red hands which he clapped from time to time, and breathed on, against the cold. "Who is this? What have we here?" the man exclaimed. It was German, but in an accent so different that the Prince, at first, understood the tone of his voice, rather than the words.

"I am Prince Erhard," he burst out. "You shall be well rewarded if you bring word to the palace that you have found me!"

The man's mocking expression reminded the Prince of

what he himself had seen in a forest pool a few days earlier. The charcoal-burner clearly thought him drunk or demented. Besides, the forest was so extensive he must have wandered from his own state. Collecting his wits, the Prince said slowly and clearly: "I am a poor wayfarer. Lost in the forest."

"Wayfarer?" the man grunted. He touched the Prince's sleeve. Stained and ragged, still it was velvet. "Some clown or mountebank," he said. "A lazy fellow, hiding himself when there is work to be done, and food and shelter to be honestly earned."

"I would gladly work, friend," the Prince rejoined. "I should be grateful to the saints for a human shelter."

"Good. Prove your words," said the charcoal-burner. "I need a helper." And he led the way to his clean, warm hut, where his wife was setting out supper, and three small children—two boys and a girl—made a merry noise that fell gratefully on the Prince's ear.

Wild and unkempt as he seemed in the glow from the hearth fire, there was something so chastened in his manner that the charcoal-burner and his wife felt compassion for him. After the filling meal, they made him a bed of clean straw in the shed behind the hut; and the woman gave him a hot brick wrapped in a rag to lay against his feet. He thanked them and lay down to a sound sleep.

He awoke at daybreak. The charcoal-burner fitted him out warmly with some old clothes of his own, gave him an axe and after a plain but plentiful breakfast, they went to his furnace in the woods. Here they worked together, day in and day out, returning only at dusk to the shelter of the hut. The Prince toiled willingly. He was glad of human company, and while he worked he was able to forget his anxieties and all that he had lost. In the evenings, the liveliness of the children and their affection kept him from relapsing into melancholy; and at night he fell into deep, dreamless sleep.

Two months passed in this way. The charcoal-burner came to like and trust him, despite his reserve and the refinement of his manners. Once or twice the Prince was sent a day's journey to the nearest village, with a load of charcoal to sell. Before returning, he walked about among the villagers and country folk, asking a question here and there, in the hope of hearing news of his own domain. But those who had even heard of such a state and city, knew it only as "far away."

At last he was driven to question the charcoal-burner. Lifting his smoke-blackened face from the pile of ash he was shoveling, he asked: "How far might it be to the principality of ——?"

The charcoal-burner wiped the sweat from his forehead with a rag of sacking and said: "Over a hundred leagues. Why, have you kinsfolk there?"

"An old aunt . . ." said the Prince hesitantly. "She was good to me."

"Is it your wish to visit her, then?"

"Yes. In the spring," said the Prince, catching at a plan of action. "I will leave you in the spring."

"Good," said the charcoal-burner. "It's wise to wait until the roads are clear."

When the bright spring weather set in, the charcoal-burner gave the Prince a purse with ten pieces of silver. The wife gave him food for the day, to carry with him. The children kissed him and waved to him until he was out of sight.

The Prince felt that his journey was well begun. No matter what bad news might be awaiting him in his own country, he was alive and well despite his strange misfortunes. He bought himself a leather jerkin, good strong shoes, and a dagger for self-defense. The money remaining would last until he could reach his own people. Eagerly he trudged along the highway.

On the fourth night of his journey, robbers raided the wayside inn where he was staying, stripped him and the other guests of all their belongings and when he fought back, beat him unconscious. Bruised and aching, he came to himself. He was penniless and still eighteen days' journey from home. But at least he was not in the depths of the forest. What he had done once, he could do again.

So he set out along the road. Wherever he found work he remained for a few days; when he had money enough to pay for food and lodging along the way, he continued his travels. The journey that should have taken not more than three weeks, lengthened itself to another two months.

At last he came to his own country, and to its capital, the seat of his court. It shocked him that he could move about unnoticed among his own people, until he came to understand that his poverty, his ragged beard and haggard face were a total disguise. Who would believe him if he were to proclaim himself?

But, being unrecognized, he could ask the questions that a stranger might naturally ask—about the former Prince, about the present ruler. . . . To his secret horror, there was no news whatever! Nothing exceptional had happened during the past year.

He had not been missed. There was some imposture. Incredibly, someone was taking his place. Who might it be? Who resembled him? His cousin? His cousin was too much older. One thing was clear, his disappearance had been kept from his people.

After a night without sleep he came early to the palace and entered that part of the grounds that was open to the public. He went as far as he might, and posted himself near the great gate leading to the private garden and park.

His heart swelled with bitter longing at the familiar sights. He could see the little summerhouse near which, under a marble slab, his old hound lay buried. He could see into the courtyard where, as a child newly able to walk, he had ridden his first pony. And there was the window through which he had gone so lightly, in pursuit of the white gazelle over six months ago.

He could see among the guardsmen on duty one or two with whom he had practised fencing. But now he knew that he must not reveal himself too soon. Who were his friends at the palace, who might be on his side against the usurper?

He was sifting his memories of the more influential courtiers, when his thoughts were arrested at sight of an old man in a dark gabardine and somber hood. The Jew, Meyer Rothfels, was slowly, as if reluctantly, leaving the palace grounds. Erhard suddenly remembered his father's words: "When you are not content with the advice of other men . . . send for Rothfels. . . . He will find a way out of your difficulty."

The Prince met him at the gate. He drew the old man aside. "As you were my father's friend, Meyer Rothfels," he said, "will you aid me now in my need?"

The old man's discerning ear and shrewd eye unraveled the disguises. "What masquerade is this?" he muttered. "What has befallen you, my Prince? But come with me. It is better that we talk privately."

Rothfels brought him to his house in the *Judengasse*, gave him a velvet suit and helped him to remove the beard and cut his neglected hair. "Now you are yourself again," the old man said, "What do you require of me?"

The Prince stared at him, astonished. "You ask me that?" he cried. "I have but one wish. Bring me into the palace that I may face the usurper and unmask him!"

Meyer Rothfels studied the Prince's face in silence for some time. Then, "Tell me what troubles you?" he said.

"Am I of such small account that since I left my palace more than six months ago, no word of my disappearance has reached my people?" And he told about that evil hour when he had started after the white gazelle and the long trail of loneliness and hardship and misfortune he had followed from that day to this.

As he mentioned his lighthearted sally after the limping

doe, his hearer's eyes widened in amazement; but the old man made no comment, though his fervent interest never slackened throughout the story.

"Now will you bring me to my successor?" the Prince demanded, rising to his feet.

"I will bring you to him."

Through a little door the Prince had never known, Meyer Rothfels led the way amid winding corridors. As they came to the part of the palace familiar to him, the Prince strode ahead to his own apartments. He hurried from one chamber to another, but found nobody except his servants. He entered his bedroom. That also was empty.

"Where is he? Where is the new Prince? Summon him here before me!" he exclaimed, as the old Jew followed at a more leisurely pace.

"This is he." Meyer Rothfels brought him to face a mirror. "You have no successor. You left the palace but an hour ago."

The Prince seated himself, for his strength failed him.

"It is a miracle! A miracle from the hand of God Himself. Blessed be He, and blessed be His name!" The old man's voice quivered like a harp string. "I saw you—I, myself—saw you leap from the window an hour ago, and follow the gazelle." He drew back the coverlets. "See, my lord, your bed is still warm."

A servant entered and, bowing, patiently asked: "Will it please the Prince to finish his breakfast?"

"How long is it—When did I leave the table?" the Prince asked carefully.

"It is more than an hour since—" The Prince dismissed him.

"Is it not written in the Psalms," Meyer Rothfels went on: " 'For a thousand years in Thy sight are but as yesterday when it is past, and as a watch in the night'? And in your own prayer, the Magnificat, you say: 'He hath put down the mighty from his seat, and hath exalted those of low degree.' Glory be to God, who preserved you unharmed!"

Silently the Prince reflected on the anguish, the vicissitudes of those vanished months. His heart filled with an enduring wonder. "By His Grace," he murmured at length, "I have learned enough for a lifetime." With fond appreciation his eyes wandered about the rich, comfortable chambers, in gratitude for all that he had not lost. On the mantel he saw the writing that would exile the Jews.

His mind returned to Meyer Rothfels. Answering the look in the old man's eloquent eyes, he rose and threw the document into the fire. "I know now what it is, to be homeless and a stranger," he said.

From then on the Prince had a friend from whom nothing need be hidden, and the people had a wise and merciful prince.

His Neighbor in Paradise

RASHI, THE FAMOUS RABBI AND COMMENTATOR, SEEKS OUT THE MAN WHO, IT WAS REVEALED, SHOULD BE NEAREST HIM IN THE WORLD TO COME.

RASHI, the eleventh-century scholar whose Old Testament commentary is valued to this day, led a tranquil life in the city of Troyes. There are no recorded events giving rise to the legends that cling about his name. They developed, it would seem, solely from the fervent admiration that pupils and colleagues felt for him.

It is said, for instance, that in later life he was visited by a haunting dream.

He saw himself in Paradise, seated in a place of honor with his wife beside him. At his other hand, leaning towards him in friendly intimacy, was a man unknown to him. The face was not clearly visible, for a wisp of cloud obscured the eyes; but the foreign style and rich material of the clothing, and the courtly, confident manner, made him seem a person quite unfamiliar in the company of scholars.

"Who is the stranger seated beside me?" Rashi asked the angel who had brought him to the scene.

"He is to be your neighbor in the World to Come."

"But who—and what—is he?"

"Don Abraham the Just, of Barcelona!" In the angelic utterance the name rang with tender meaning.

It echoed in Rashi's mind as he awoke. "Don Abraham the Just, of Barcelona! I know of no such person," Rashi pondered. "Yet exalted he must be—high in attainment— to be so proclaimed among the angels."

There were two or three students from Spain at his academy. Rashi questioned them subtly about the distinguished men of the Spanish communities, Barcelona among them. But no Don Abraham came to light. Rashi spent more time with passing travelers from the west, but no trace or mention of the man so real in his vision came to prove that this person existed.

"I will seek him out," Rashi decided.

He made ready for a secret journey. It was not unusual in those times, for a learned man to retire from his customary place and go on a solitary pilgrimage, either as spiritual discipline or in search of further learning, unhampered by his eminence. With an assumed name and unattended, Rashi traveled humbly from one Jewish community to another, across the width of France. In synagogue and house of study, he joined the students, listening to discussions among teachers, rabbis and dignitaries. But there was never any mention of Abraham of Barcelona.

He crossed into Spain. His Spanish might be less than perfect, but the Hebrew tongue was an unfailing bond among medieval scholars. Here the learned men of Barcelona were known and lauded, but never a Don Abraham among them.

Rashi arrived in Barcelona. He entered the chief synagogue and was made welcome, according to ancient custom. He listened again, expectantly, for some word about his companion in Paradise. To his surprise, the man whose fame must have reached Heaven, seemed to be unknown in his own city.

At last, Rashi mentioned that he would like to make the acquaintance of Don Abraham the Just.

"We know of a Don Abraham," the rabbi answered, "but not by any opinion could he be called 'righteous' or 'just.' He is charitable, yes. But he is worldly, extravagant, and though accepted at court, he gives us little cause to be proud of him."

More curious than ever, Rashi persisted. He was directed to the house of Don Abraham.

It was a mansion with a garden court cooled by fountains and the shade of flowering trees. As Rashi entered, the marble stairways, the heathenish paintings, the lavish display of wealth astonished him. Worldly and extravagant he is, Rashi thought.

However, there was nothing of ostentation about the

personable middle-aged man who received him and bade him welcome.

"A scholar from France?" Don Abraham queried. "And you were commended to me?"

"By a high authority. Since when I have come on purpose to meet you."

"You come at a good time," Don Abraham rejoined. "Tomorrow, I am to be married."

Rashi congratulated him, quoting from Proverbs:

> Whoso findeth a wife findeth a great good,
> And obtaineth favor of the Lord.

"But how great is the favor!" Don Abraham exclaimed, his eyes moist with happiness. "She is such a maiden as I had hoped for, but never before found. Beautiful, virtuous, with an understanding mind— But you shall see her and judge for yourself. You must be my guest while you remain in Barcelona."

And Don Abraham led him to a fine apartment, and remained with him while he settled his few belongings. Then they ate together, and the host said: "I wish I could give you all my attention. But there are many things to be prepared for the morrow. Will you accompany me while I see the arrangements carried out?"

This was exactly what Rashi wanted, to know Don Abraham as he went about his affairs. The steward escorted them through the linen rooms, the silver storehouse, the wine cellar. Here Rashi, who, living in the Champagne district, had always supported his family by winemaking, approved his host's discriminating taste. When everything was planned to the last detail, Don Abraham turned to his guest and said: "Have I wearied you? Or shall we greet some old friends, for whom I keep this hour?"

"Let me go with you," said Rashi.

They came into a large, cheerful suite, comfortably furnished yet with no ostentation. It had its own entrance from the courtyard. Here were gathered in ones and twos and family groupings, the people who benefited by Don Abraham's philanthropy. Rashi noticed that attendants served them as of custom with wine and fruit and sweet-meats. They were treated like guests, not suppliants. There was but one expression on the faces of all, as Don Abraham entered. It was a rare affection that shone on him and wished him joy.

As he went from one group to another, Rashi gathered the story of each. One young man had completed his training as a craftsman, another was learning to be a physician. There were children who had been nurtured through dangerous illness. An old man and woman whose little home had been destroyed by fire, were never done with thanking Don Abraham for rebuilding and refurnishing it. To each he was a friend. He entered into their lives and restored courage and good faith. They had come today to make no request, only to honor and congratulate him.

When they had all left and Don Abraham was turning to the door, a woman dressed and veiled in black came from behind a pillar and confronted him. "Don Abraham," she begged, in a tone that was almost a sob, "I have a great . . . a presumptuous request to make. . . ."

He bowed. "Ask, madame," he said. "I can refuse you nothing today!"

But the gracious reply merely unnerved her. She could do nothing but weep. Don Abraham brought her to a chair, seated himself beside her and waited until she could speak. "It is my son's life that I despair of," she said at length. "He is sick unto death."

"My physician shall go to him at once," said Don Abraham. "But remember, friend, life and death are in God's hand."

"It is no ailment for a physician to cure," she said with tremulous boldness. "He is dying for love. This is my eldest son, who since his father's death has been my support and the kind guardian of the family. He was betrothed to a young girl, a neighbor's daughter, whom he has loved since childhood. But the match has been broken off, for a more advantageous marriage."

Don Abraham remarked thoughtfully: "This is not the first time that vows have been broken, and a maiden has proved false."

"No, señor. It is not in my heart to blame the maiden. She is a sweet child and would be true to him. But the new bridegroom is a man of wealth and can lift her family to better standing. He is worthy and well esteemed. The marriage would provide education for her brothers, peace and rest for her parents, good matches for her sisters. . . . How can she do other than accept such good fortune?"

"Cannot your son accept it?"

"He gave up his claim and set her free. To do more is beyond his power, though he has striven for courage. I have seen his strength fail, day by day. Food and sleep became impossible to him. Now he lies in a trance, waiting for death."

"Who is the new bridegroom," Don Abraham asked. "Perhaps I might intercede for the young man, your son."

The mother flung herself at Don Abraham's feet, her arms about his knees. "It is you, Don Abraham. It is you!" she wailed.

Don Abraham sat in silence for a while. Then he raised the woman to her feet. "Tell me how I may reach your son," he said composedly. "I shall speak with him as his father might, and bring to mind the duty he owes you and his family. He will resign himself to God's will, and thus be restored to you, never fear." The mother was sent away, unconsoled.

"Such are the sorrows of life," said Don Abraham to his guest. "We must learn to endure them." And he went about his other preparations, making no further reference to his young rival's fate.

Rashi was shocked, for he had begun to feel a strong liking for the worldly Don Abraham. Now he saw that pride of power and callousness at the point where another's misfortune touched his own well-being, were also a part of this man's character.

The following day, Don Abraham supervised the final arrangements in the garden court, where the wedding ceremony was to take place. He was genial to guest and servitors alike.

When the bride's party arrived, Rashi saw that she justi-

fied her bridegroom's praise. She was more than beautiful, with luminous dark eyes that gave life to a face of white rose pallor. She graced her sumptuous dress by her indifference to it.

More and more guests arrived. The shaded archways and garden recesses were fully taken up with a rustling, gleaming company. Presently Don Abraham stepped towards the entrance gate and greeted a tall young man, gaunt with recent illness, at sight of whom the bride turned her face away quickly, to hide the rush of tears and the quivering blush.

"Our party is complete now," Don Abraham announced. "Set up the *huppah!*"

And while attendants hastened to erect the silken, gold-fringed wedding canopy, he said: "Let me see the marriage contract."

He studied it, with the stately *haham* beside him, and remarked: "As I thought, there is an error here. The bridegroom is Elijah Reubeni, I am merely the go-between, the matchmaker." He watched while the corrections were made. Then Don Abraham led the young man to his place beneath the canopy.

The happiness in the radiant eyes of the bride and bridegroom pervaded the entire gathering in a blissful hush, as the ceremony proceeded.

When it was completed Don Abraham escorted the young couple to a carriage, and they were borne away to their new home—a small estate, the deed to which Don Abraham had placed in the bridegroom's hand as a wedding gift.

Now the festivities began. Don Abraham was everywhere. Rashi watched him fondly, enjoying his share in the life and future of this man. He was an ideal host. He made graceful speeches in answer to the toasts. He laughed at the gaieties of the witty. He led the dances until they went on without him. He had guttering tapers replaced, tables cleared and set with fresh flowers and dainties, winecups refilled. He chatted with the older guests, as they sat enjoying the fragrant breezes of evening.

It was so great a success that not until well past midnight did the company dissolve. Then as the last carriage rolled away and the last footfalls retreated, Don Abraham seated himself at a small table beside Rashi.

"We will have a little wine," he said, filling both goblets. He passed a hand over his face, and his head sank forward on his breast.

"Now I know why the angel spoke of you as Don Abraham the Just," said Rashi.

"Angel? What angel?" Don Abraham looked at him indulgently.

"It was not my true name that I gave you," said his guest. "I am Rashi."

"Rashi of Troyes!" the other exclaimed. "One need not be a scholar to know that name. And you have come, in disguise, so far?"

"To seek you out," said Rashi. And he related his dream.

Don Abraham smiled wistfully. "I look forward to it," he said. "When a man is alone, he needs a pleasant neighbor, even there. . . ."

A Problem for
Maimonides

THE GREATEST PHYSICIAN OF HIS TIME IS
SEIZED WITH PANIC WHILE OPERATING.

RABBI MOSES BEN MAIMON, better
known as Maimonides, had chosen the practice of medicine
as his livelihood. Like Rashi and other scholars of the
period, he did not accept payment for teaching the Torah,
or for his post of honor as rabbi and head of his community.

When he was obliged to flee from Moslem fanaticism
in Spain, he found a home in Fostat—twelfth-century
Cairo—and in time was singled out to attend Sultan Saladin
the Magnanimous, his family and his court. It is even
fancied that Saladin sent him to cure a fever of which
Richard the Lion-hearted had fallen ill.

As his fame spread, sick people were brought from other
lands, and young men traveled from every civilized country hoping to study under him. He could accept only a cer-

tain number of pupils, however, and the beginning of each year saw an inflow of candidates only the first-come of whom could be admitted to his lectures. The others had to postpone their plans or give them up entirely. Most of the disappointed students drifted away.

But one young man from a faraway land, whose arrival had been long delayed by storm and misadventure, could not accept the fact that the class was full and he must wait two more years. He could not bring himself to leave this city of his hopes. Determined to find some way of hearing the lectures, he haunted the neighborhood where the great physician lived.

It was not long before he found a crevice he could squeeze through. Maimonides was looking for a discreet, able-bodied servant to attend him everywhere—on his cases, to the lectures and to the Sultan's palace.

The young stranger applied for this position. It occurred to him that he would have a better chance if he pretended to be mute. For that would give him an advantage on the score of discretion. His plan succeeded. When he presented the written statement of his qualifications and willingness, Maimonides considered also the fact that, as a mute, the young man would be admitted without difficulty to the Sultan's palace.

"I will try you for a few days," he decided.

The few days became years. Maimonides found his new attendant helpful and able beyond all expectation. The dumb servant went with him everywhere, almost as much attached to him as his shadow.

The young man, for his part, was delighted. Here was a better chance of learning than he had ever anticipated. He was present at the lectures from their beginning, when he heard Maimonides declare: "To be a good physician, one must possess three things: knowledge, observation, and an open mind. . . ."

He carried his master's instruments and books and medicines, standing by and occasionally helping while the physician treated his patients for mild complaints or in serious illness. There was no end to the experience he gained. Maimonides rose at dawn in order to reach the Sultan's palace in good time, for the way was lined with the poor of the city, whom he examined and advised with the same care that he lavished on the great ones.

The young man frequently listened to discussions between his master and distinguished friends. The topics ranged beyond medicine, to the philosophy of Aristotle— on which Maimonides was the leading authority—to Jewish ethics, in which again he was pre-eminent, to comparative religion and the entire world of ideas. It was an education such as the silent student had never dreamed of. And since he was allowed in his spare time to use his master's library, his knowledge grew fast and his mind developed at an amazing rate.

Furthermore, the writings of Maimonides were open to him. Almost as soon as they were formulated, he read such thoughts as these:

The sincere believers of every creed will share in the joys of the World to Come. . . . God looks into our hearts and

[139]

judges us, not according to our belief but according to our honesty. He sheds His blessing equally upon the noble Gentile and the pious Jew. . . . The sincerest prayer is the prayer of the hands. The way to Heaven is paved not with holy words, but with worthy deeds.

His respect and love for the man at whose service he had placed himself, increased to devotion. Imperceptibly the student ceased to think of his own advantage. Rather, he sought ways of furthering his teacher's effectiveness.

A dilemma arose in which it was he who found the solution.

The Sultan's favorite daughter fell ill. She complained of a gnawing headache which gave her hardly a moment's peace, day or night. Maimonides, after thorough examination and study of the case, found that she was suffering from a very rare ailment. A tiny worm had found its way, perhaps through her nose or mouth, into the cavity of the skull, and was now moving about over her brain. The only remedy was to cut into the brainpan and remove the creature.

Before undertaking the dangerous operation, Maimonides asked permission to consult several other experienced doctors. If they should agree with his diagnosis, he would do anything that offered a chance to cure her. The physicians all confirmed his judgment, agreeing that the only hope was to operate.

Maimonides asked that he and his dumb servant be left alone with the patient, who was now insensible from pain and exhaustion.

The physician was troubled as never before. So much depended on his success. The life of the fair young girl, so dear to her father. Probably the Sultan's friendship for himself, and continued protection for the Jews. The bitter and envious intrigues ever-present in the palace might, if he failed to save her, overthrow all that Maimonides had built up.

With a prayer for guidance, he selected a trepan from the instruments laid out by his servant and skillfully opened the skull, laying bare a section of the brain.

He was right. A tiny worm wriggled about on its surface, disturbed at being exposed to the light. But how to get it out, without injuring the delicate and important tissues?

Maimonides took up his finest pair of forceps, bent over to remove the worm—but stopped, for fear the creature, in trying to escape, should bury itself in the brain. He laid down the forceps. His forehead stung with perspiration, under the anguish of decision. For he must act quickly. To hide from the sudden light, the worm might crawl into the skull's recesses. What must he do? How get it out?

"Try this, master," said a voice. A green leaf from one of the plants in the room, was laid in the physician's hand.

Maimonides held the leaf close above the incision. Attracted by the fresh odor, the worm reared its head and, crawling onto the edge of the leaf, little by little came away from the brain.

Maimonides completed the operation rapidly, bandaged the head, and called in the girl's attendants to carry her back to her chamber.

Then, relieved and free to relax, he realized suddenly that the dumb servant had spoken. He laid his hands on the young man's shoulders. "You are no mute!" he cried. "Why the pretense? Who are you?"

The servant told his story amid the wondering, delighted comments of his teacher.

"But you are now a better physician than I," said Maimonides. "You can no longer pose as my lackey. I shall see to it that you are received as my colleague.

And so, indeed, Maimonides lost a valued servant, but acquired a lifelong partner and friend.

The Clay Guardian

RABBI JUDAH LOEW DEFENDS HIS PEO-
PLE AGAINST THE BLOOD ACCUSATION.

IN the later years of his life, Rabbi Judah Loew fashioned a *golem*—a living, yet incomplete being—to serve as a protector of his people.

At that time the Jews of Prague lived in constant fear of the Blood Accusation. It was not the fault of the Church. Johann Sylvester, the cardinal, had publicly taken Rabbi Loew's hand and thanked him for his answers to the written questions submitted by a convocation of priests. All had pledged their friendship to the Jewish community.

Still, among the people, the hideous belief was spreading that the Jews required Christian blood in celebrating their Passover and would commit ritual murder to obtain it. The months between the two spring festivals, Purim—the Feast of Esther—and Passover itself, had become a time of dread, when riotous crowds were disbanded and false judgments averted only by the vigilant wisdom of Rabbi Loew and the respect felt for him by the legal authorities.

The rabbi had no doubt that an astute central mind was at work, plotting the destruction of his people. But how to avert the growing danger and unearth the enemy?

Rabbi Judah turned to his mystical studies, and after long fasts and ardent prayer, presented a "dream question" to Heaven.

He was answered in a dream. An array of familiar household objects, each with an aura of significance, provided him with a list of initial letters. Arranging these according to formulae in the abstruse Book of Creation, he arrived at one conclusion:

Make a golem of clay and you will destroy the destroyers.

From the *Kabbalah*, the occult theosophic teaching based on mystic interpretation of the Scriptures, he worked out his instructions for the awesome task. He took into his confidence Isaac ben Samson, his son-in-law, and Jacob ben Hayim Sasson, a devoted pupil. The former was a *Kohen*—descended from the family of Aaron, the first high priest —and the latter a Levite, whose ancestors belonged to the tribe of Levi, the lesser rank in the Biblical priesthood. (This ancient lineage, with its duties and prohibitions handed down through centuries from father to son, had a special importance for Rabbi Judah's purpose.) They purified themselves by prayer and fasting and immersion in the ritual bath of running water. Then on a certain night, they went down to a bed of clay beside the River Moldau.

By the light of torches, chanting Psalms, they moulded

a clay figure three ells long. When the Kohen paced around it, uttering charms, the image reddened and glowed as if in a fire. When the Levite walked about it, taking the opposite direction, the charms he spoke washed away the heat. Water flowed through the clay man, nails appeared on his extremities and hair sprouted from his head. Rabbi Judah bent above the prostrate figure, inscribing on its forehead *E'mes,* a name of God meaning "Truth." The image moved slightly, separating itself from the bed of clay.

They bowed to the four points of the compass and recited in unison: "And He breathed into his nostrils the breath of life; and man became a living soul." The golem opened its eyes and looked around in astonishment.

"I name thee Joseph," the rabbi intoned. The creature nodded. "Arise, Joseph, and stand before me!" With a hinged, yet not ungainly movement, it stood up towering almost twice the height of the tall rabbi. They dressed him in clothes they had prepared for him, clothes suitable to a caretaker.

Again the rabbi spoke: "Thou, Joseph, must obey my commands and do my bidding." Bowing his head, Joseph made gestures of willingness. "Good," said the rabbi. "Now follow us."

It was still completely dark when they reached the Jews' Quarter. A bed was prepared for the golem in the rabbi's house; and there he stayed.

Gradually he became a familiar figure to the dwellers in the ghetto, who looked on him with respect and kept their distance. Rabbi Judah's household, too, had been warned that they must not use him for private or worldly errands. His sole task was to guard the Jews against persecution.

Thus, the golem paced the outskirts of the Jews' Quarter at night, watching for reckless idlers or groups that aroused suspicion, when he would at once bring word to the rabbi. Though Joseph was dumb, his gestures spoke for him. Or, if need be, he wrote down in Hebrew what he had observed.

Sometimes, receiving such a report, Rabbi Judah sent him on a secret investigation, to follow and watch suspected enemies. He fastened an amulet to Joseph's breast making him invisible, and the golem would steal away on his errand, moving soundlessly despite his size and weight.

One year, the citizens of Prague were aroused to great anxiety by the disappearance of a Christian maidservant who had been employed at kindling fires and lighting lamps for the Jews on their Sabbath. A Jewish tailor was accused of ritual murder; and a certain monk, Thaddeus, preached a powerful sermon in which the girl was portrayed as a holy martyr. Thaddeus quickly became famous for his eloquence and fervor.

Witnesses affirmed at the trial that they had seen the maid, bound and helpless, in the tailor's cellar. The man's own stepdaughter swore that the phials of blood displayed in evidence had been drawn from the Christian girl's veins. And while the realized horrors stifled the breath of those assembled, Joseph Golem drove up to the courthouse with the missing maid, safe and well, on the wagon-seat beside him! She had left without word for employment in a distant village; but Rabbi Judah had sent the golem in search of her, with a letter that decided her to come back with him.

At another period, when the special flour for the Passover unleavened bread was late in arriving, many in the community volunteered to help with the *matzoh*-baking. Two Gentile baker's apprentices pleaded for work and were given employment removing the finished matzos from the ovens.

Joseph Golem, having no special task, was present at the cheerful scene, and the baker in charge of the work amiably gave him some of the first matzos to taste. By the time he reached home, however, the golem had become very sick, and showed the rabbi by his gestures that he suffered severe pains in his stomach. Rabbi Judah healed him with a touch; then ordered all work on the matzoh-baking suspended.

As part of the careful inquiry by the rabbi, the golem was sent to search the lodgings of the apprentices. He brought back a casket half full of a powder that proved to be poison; and one of the young men, under promise of secrecy, confessed to the rabbi that Thaddeus had given him the powder and told him it would be praiseworthy to play a joke on the enemies of Heaven. The apprentice wept that he had brought harm on people who had been good to him.

Rabbi Judah now realized that the monk Thaddeus might be the person giving focus and force to the popular hostility against the Jews. His sermons were inflammatory, yet in his personal dealings he was genial and persuasive. More than any other priest, he was a familiar sight in the ghetto, for he conducted some of the business for his monastery and it took him among the Jews.

It was the wealthy and respected Jewish merchant Michael Berger, who kept the wine cellars of the monastery supplied. Berger had an only daughter, Rahel, who was a most unusual girl not only for her beauty but her mental quality and character. Berger, in appreciation of her gifts, had seen to it that she received the finest education possible in those times. She knew Hebrew and Latin and Greek. She could sing sweetly and accompany herself on the lute; yet she was very capable in practical matters, and took an interest in her father's trade. Her precocity was such that, at the age of seventeen, she kept the books of the wine shop and often relieved her father during business hours.

When Thaddeus came to know Rahel, it became a matter of sincere grief to him that this radiant child was a lost soul. If only he could deliver her to the mercy and salvation of the Church!

He conceived a subtle plan to bring this about. One day, while her father was occupied at the warehouse, Thaddeus sent word to Rahel that a mistake had been made in the reckoning for the last supply of Malaga, and that some bottles of it were not so good as usual. Rahel's pride was hurt, since she kept the books. Besides, Thaddeus was an important customer. Impatient, and not wishing to trouble her father, Rahel ordered another case of the suspected wine to be loaded on a wagonette and, accompanied by a servant, drove to the monastery.

It was situated on the wide, handsome Street of the Dominicans. Expressing cordial pleasure at her quick attention to his complaint, Thaddeus offered her the wine to taste. It turned out that these bottles were in no way inferior; and a search among his papers produced a mislaid statement and receipt that had made his reckoning faulty.

Thaddeus, with many apologies, detained her, chatting pleasantly about affairs of general interest, that fed her eager mind, yet awakened a craving for more knowledge. He left her alone for a while, saying that he must report the errors he had made.

Rahel rose and went to one of the long windows. Music drifted from the mansion and garden across the way, where, it seemed, noble guests were being entertained. Wistfully, Rahel wondered at the unburdened life of such as these, and the brilliant scenes and courtly companions with which it was blessed. Half-unconsciously she stepped through the window onto the balcony and gazed, lost in daydreams, at the alluring vista.

Presently, an agile young man appeared and crossed toward the monastery as if about to enter. But he halted near the balcony, looking up at her in wonder. A strange sweet pain entered her heart, as though it had flown at her from his glowing eyes. She felt herself flush as he removed his cap and bowed low.

By that time Thaddeus had returned. Rahel stepped back from the balcony feeling somewhat dizzy. Thaddeus, however, was pleased at the young man's arrival, called down to him that he would soon be at liberty and invited him to enter. As Rahel made ready to leave, Thaddeus explained that the young Count Waldberg was a former pupil of his, and had just completed his more advanced studies in Paris.

At home again, Rahel's contentment had vanished. She was dutiful as ever and gave no outward sign of the change in her outlook. Yet her life now seemed narrow and limited, without brightness or color. Her only joy was the contact with Thaddeus who always sent her little personal notes along with the business communications which had become, to her satisfaction, much more frequent. Occasionally, he made mention of Count Ladislaus Waldberg and his admirable nature. At one time he wrote that the Count remembered her and had asked after her welfare.

It was a dazzling spring day, overwarm and stirring with life, when Rahel was seized with an impulse that she could not resist and dared not examine. She walked as if in a dream through the tree-lined street that led to the Moldau bridge, crossed the river and came to the Street of the Dominicans. In front of the monastery she looked about, as if fearing that she had been followed, then knocked at the door.

She asked to see Thaddeus and was admitted. It was a relief to her that he was not surprised at her coming. He accepted it as natural that she should wish to leave the ghetto and enter a new life under the protection of the Church. A comfortable lodging nearby was made ready for her, and Thaddeus himself undertook to instruct her in the Christian faith.

It was not many days before Rahel was overtaken by her conscience. It became clear to her that she had been moved, not so much by the wish for her soul's salvation, as by the advantages and new avenues that conversion would open to her. She suffered, too, at thought of her parents' grief and anxiety.

Thaddeus, observing her troubled mood, saw that, naturally under the circumstances, she was haunted by loneliness. He told her that now he felt free to speak of the young Count's interest in her. Not only that, but he, Thaddeus, was planning a festive supper at which Ladislaus and his father were to be the other guests. Rahel was captivated. She thought of little else.

Meanwhile Thaddeus knew that she must be moved to a safer retreat. For Rahel's father was seeking her everywhere, and using all means at his command to get some knowledge of her whereabouts. Earlier that day, Thaddeus himself had promised the desperate parents all the assistance in his power, at the same time denying that he knew anything about their daughter's disappearance.

An underground passage connected the wine cellars below the monastery with an ancient, mouldering palace at the crossroads not far from the Jews' Quarter. It was immemorially old, a ruin on three sides. But an eccentric ruler of former years had rebuilt one wing of it and taken up his abode deep in its recesses, living unseen by his people. To this secret dwelling place Rahel was removed, with the clothes and music and embroidery work and books of devotion that had been lavishly provided for her.

Rabbi Judah Loew was troubled by a recurrent dream of the ruined palace. Three nights in succession he saw it. Once, with fire eating away its foundations. In the second dream lightning struck it and set it ablaze. In the third, a seraph—a flaming spirit—flew among the rafters, trailing fiery wings.

Rabbi Judah knew it for a warning.

Thaddeus was host at an exquisite supper in honor of Count Waldberg and his son. Rahel, accustomed to the plain costume of the ghetto, regulated by law, was surprised at her own beauty in the trailing gown of crimson brocade, with pearls braided in her long black hair. They sat together for hours, lost in discussion, and exploring plans that seemed to her delightful, enchanting. The young Count could not take his eyes from Rahel, while the older nobleman found himself completely won by her beauty, intelligence, and fine bearing.

A lull occurred in the general talk. Then Ladislaus asked that his father might approve of his suit for Rahel's hand. It was decided there and then, that in two months' time, when her religious instruction should be completed, Rahel was to receive baptism. And on the same day, said Thaddeus, the marriage might take place.

Ladislaus kissed the hands of his betrothed and placed on her finger a ring that was an heirloom, graven with the heraldic arms of his house.

Rahel could not sleep that night. Happiness intoxicated her, such happiness as she had never hoped for. Too restless to remain in one place, she clothed herself and walked about the rich, strange apartment. Leaving its door open, she wandered through the long corridors, looking for a window. She wanted to see the sky, to breathe the air.

But there was no opening to the outside world until she descended into a long, ruinous gallery around three sides of an old hall. Here were great semicircular archways open to the night. The sky was dark and misty, without a star. But the cool air was pleasant on her heated forehead and cheeks. She breathed it in, loath to return.

She became conscious that footsteps were entering the hall below. Realizing her imprudence, she crouched down close to the railing of the gallery and noiselessly waited for the intruders to go.

But they were talking. She heard the voice of Thaddeus. "At daybreak," he was saying, "we shall begin a search of the Jews' Quarter, and as we return, we shall step aside here . . ."

"And make our discovery," another man said.

At that moment the moon broke through the clouds. A bright beam illuminated one archway, and one section of the hall. Peering from the shadow Rahel, with a shrinking tremor, saw the face of Thaddeus as she had never seen it before. He took a bundle from one of his followers and laid it down on a pile of debris. The tone of his voice appalled her. "Now let the Jews escape our charge! Damnation take them!"

"Amen!" the others rejoined.

Some time after they left she found strength enough to descend the crumbling stairway. While still at a distance she recognized the familiar border, striped blue and white, of the fringed prayer shawl. With trembling hands she drew it back from what it covered—the dead body of a child, newly disinterred, and pierced at the throat in pretence that its blood had been drained until it died.

The moonbeam disappeared. In darkness of heart, Rahel seated herself on the stairway. Her lofty visions of bliss were snatched away. Ladislaus, who spoke her name so sweetly, and who gazed at her with such worshipful love in his honest, nobly venturesome eyes, was not for her. His was not her world. She could not stand with Thaddeus, the false accuser, the destroyer of her people. This was her place; beside the small, mistreated corpse, with the smear of dried blood tarnishing the silver cross around its neck. . . .

Again footsteps were approaching. But Rahel did not care to hide. She raised her eyes listlessly towards the new-comers, and to her amazement saw a lantern swinging from the broad shoulders and massive height of the golem. Straight to the child's body he went, stood before it, then turned to beckon the rabbi. Wearily, though erect as ever, the old man drew near.

"This, then, was the meaning of my dreams," he uttered. "Who, now, is to be our accuser?"

Rahel rose to her feet. "Rabbi," she said, "it is Thaddeus. I saw him place it there. I heard him say . . ." Her strength left her and she fell unconscious.

"Rahel Berger!" Rabbi Judah exclaimed. "Praise to the Ever-Present!" At his order, the golem bent and, lifting Rahel, drew her within his cloak and strode away home.

"So this is the abomination that, by God's judgment,

must be consumed in flame," the rabbi murmured. Not only would the Accusation be averted, but Rahel Berger would be safe from pursuit. It would seem to all that she had perished in the fire.

Rabbi Judah faced the ancient ruin. With hands extended he softly intoned a cabalistic spell. Soon the seraph he had seen in his dreams alighted on the roof, and trailing her wings among the rafters, set the wreck afire.

Rabbi Judah sent for Rahel's parents. Overjoyed at her return, they realized that for her own safety and the peace of all, she must leave the country. That same night she was sent on her way to Amsterdam, where Michael Berger's brother lived. She joined her uncle's family and her return to the ghetto remained a secret.

Some who tell the story say that Ladislaus could not be consoled for his beloved's tragic death. To distract his melancholy, his father sent him to Venice, hoping that the brilliant society of that matchless city would arouse him to new interests and a new love. But Venice failed to cure him. Secretly, in the guise of a poor student, he made his way back to Prague and sought out Rabbi Judah. To him Ladislaus insisted that he wished to become a Jew—that he felt drawn to Rahel's people, and hoped to be reunited with her.

"It is not well to change your faith," the rabbi warned him. Then, yielding to the young man's incessant appeals, Judah Loew sent him to the rabbi of Freiburg, who was related to Rahel and knew that she was alive and where she had gone.

The rabbi of Freiburg also refused him conversion, and,

to turn him away, prescribed a long course of study. After years of close application, Ladislaus was still determined. He was allowed to enter the congregation of Israel; and, won by his steadfastness, the rabbi of Freiburg advised him to make a journey to Amsterdam, where he might find his predestined mate.

"The only mate for me," said the young Count firmly, "is a maiden named Rahel."

"I know of such a maiden," the rabbi replied. "Her name is Rahel. She is related to me. Go, seek her out. It is not good for a man to live alone."

Ladislaus went to Amsterdam with a letter of introduction and paid his respects at the house of the relatives. The maiden named Rahel was veiled as she entered the room. He was presented to her, and when he bowed in greeting, she held out her hand. On it was the ring he had given his betrothed; and at the first sound of her voice, he knew her. When she raised the veil, he fell at her feet overcome with joy.

They were married; and, it is said, when the old Count died a year or so later, Ladislaus and Rahel took up their abode on the country estate, and lived there in perfect happiness to a great old age.

As for Thaddeus, the destruction of his plot and the death, as he supposed, of his pupil and convert, did not turn him from his mad purpose. Rather, he became bitter and reckless. It was not long before he betrayed himself and, caught in a criminal conspiracy, was unfrocked and sentenced to ten years' imprisonment.

Meanwhile, the golem succeeded in the purpose for which he had been created. As time went by, the rabbi recorded the proceedings brought against the Jews on charges of ritual murder and showed how in every case the evidence proved false and the accusation unfounded. Requesting an audience, he sent the chronicle to Emperor Rudolf II. Ten days went by, then a royal coach arrived at Rabbi Judah's house, to bring him to the palace.

Shortly after their conference, a decree was issued. The Emperor, it stated, was fully satisfied that the accusation of ritual murder against the Jews was false; that the Jews did not need blood for religious ceremonies; that, actually, the use of blood was a grave offense against the Jewish religion. In the future, if a Christian wished to raise such an accusation, it must be brought against the individual Jew who was alleged to be the evil-doer, and not against the Jews in general. Moreover, the facts must be established by four witnesses of acknowledged integrity; and the rabbi and representatives of the Jewish community must be present at the trial and all such proceedings.

In the ghetto there was great rejoicing over the Emperor's proclamation. All work was halted and the Jews flocked to the synagogue for a service of thanksgiving. Tables were brought out, and a feast made ready. It was a time of glad reassurance and contentment. Rabbi Judah himself felt that a burden had been lifted from him. He rested from his constant vigilance and was at peace.

Once, on the eve of Sabbath, he even forgot to give Joseph Golem his orders for the day of rest. Usually, Rabbi

Judah gave him no task, but told him merely to walk about and stand guard.

This Sabbath, however, with no orders to follow, the golem strayed about among the houses. He was attracted by a plant blooming on a windowsill and plucked it up. The woman who owned it reproved him. He scowled and overset all the other pots. Then, roused to indefinite anger, he went about pulling down the signs above shop entrances, overturning vessels and forcing doors.

Frightened children ran to Rabbi Judah, who had begun the morning services. The rabbi smote his forehead, in anger at his forgetfulness. Then he shouted aloud: "Joseph, stand still until I come to you."

The golem immediately stopped his mischief and waited, still as a statue, until Judah Loew arrived. The rabbi sent him home to sleep until sundown.

When the Sabbath was over, Rabbi Judah told Joseph to take his bed and sleep that night in the attic above the synagogue. He then called his son-in-law the Kohen, and his pupil, the Levite. "We no longer have need of him," Judah Loew said, "and he must not be misused. Had I not stopped him, he might have destroyed the *Judengasse*."

Together they went to the synagogue and ascended the stairs. They stood before the golem and prayed for some time, in silence. Then Rabbi Judah erased from its forehead the first letter of the Name. Instead of *E'mes*— "Truth"—the characters now spelled *Mes*—"Dead." The figure ceased to breathe. It stiffened and became lifeless clay again.

They concealed it beneath the worn-out *tallesim* and torn, yellowed prayer books that were kept here. And the rabbi forbade anyone to mount the staircase and enter the attic from that time on.

Only the successor to Rabbi Judah Loew's post may, when he first takes office, go up and look upon the golem. But he must not touch it or make any attempt to give it life.

And there it lies hidden to this day, in the uppermost story of the *Altneushule*. But when all souls shall come to judgment, it is said that the golem, too, shall arise and be given his fill of life, though in quite a different form.

Plucking the Rooster

AN UNPROMISING ENCOUNTER ENDS
IN A CONTEST OF WITS.

THERE was once a *poritz* (a wealthy land-owner) in Poland, whose estate was managed by a surly and quarrelsome steward. This man was unpopular with all the poritz's tenants and employees, and especially with the Jews, to whom he was most unjust.

The poritz, on the other hand, was a clever, kindly person, very easygoing. The peasants and laborers knew that if they could reach the poritz with their troubles he would treat them fairly. The great man would joke with them and ask after their families and offer them something good to drink. But it was not often that they could get to him. The manager was always on the watch for "grumblers" and when he caught them, made it so unpleasant that they found themselves worse off than ever.

One very cold day in the winter the landowner was driving about his estate in a luxurious sleigh. He was wrapped in a huge fur coat, with a fur hat which allowed only his nose and a scrap of his forehead to show. He wore thick gloves and fur-lined boots. His manager, also very warmly dressed, was seated beside him. Presently, they came upon a ragged, half-naked Jew breaking a pile of rocks which he had first cleared of ice and snow. His shirt and trousers were torn. His boots let in the snow and his hands were bare. Yet he seemed very cheerful and sang and chuckled at his work.

The poritz ordered the driver to stop and asked the manager to call the Jew before him. "My good man," the poritz said, "how can you bear to be so lightly dressed in this terrible frost?"

"*Panninkeh*," said the Jew amiably, "how can your lordship's nose bear it?"

"My nose," said the poritz, rubbing it, "is already used to the cold."

"It is that way with me; my whole body is made of nose!"

Laughing, the poritz stepped out of his carriage to chat with this strange character. The manager became impatient and looked at the Jew with no friendly eye. He could not make out what they were talking about, but both seemed to find pleasure in it.

At last the poritz said to the stone-breaker: "Yes, I can see that you're no idler. But after all, which is more—seven or five?"

"Thirty-two is still more," replied the Jew promptly.

"True," said the poritz. "But it's strange for a man like you to be so situated. Has your house burned down lately?"

"Twice, your lordship. My house has burned down twice. And what's more, I expect another fire soon."

"Your honor," the manager interrupted, "we have far to go and much to do. Talking is all very well but—"

The poritz gave him a quick glance, then turning back to the Jew went on with the conversation. Presently he said: "In how many handfuls could one pluck the rooster?"

The Jew rubbed his beard thoughtfully. "Anyone could manage it in three handfuls," he said, "but I would undertake to do it in two."

Again the poritz laughed. Still chuckling, he took his place in the sleigh. "There's nothing I enjoy more," he said as they drove away, "than a talk with a clever fellow. It's something I rarely have the chance for, since I left Warsaw and came to live on my estate."

"If your honor thinks that a barefoot ragamuffin of a Jew is a pleasant person to converse with," said the manager, offended, "then all I can say is that I don't agree."

"Of course you don't agree!" said the poritz, with more than a touch of sarcasm. "Our conversation was beyond you. You couldn't understand it."

"*I* not able to understand it! Really, your honor has a poor opinion of me. *I* not able to exchange words with a Jewish stone-breaker! Then why am I your manager?"

"Because, for the present, I have found no one to replace you. But since you think yourself superior to the Jew, tell me what we were talking about. Did you understand the

first question that I asked him? Do you know what he meant when he answered me?"

"Your honor, my mind was on something else at the moment. You can take it easy, but I have your business to think of."

"That may be," said the poritz. "But still I think that if you had the mind to appreciate the Jew's cleverness, you couldn't have helped being struck by it."

"There was nothing to be struck by, your honor. What, after all, did he say? If I had a little time to think it over, I could easily show you that I understand very well what he said."

"Take a week to think about it," said the poritz. "On Sunday after mass, you shall tell me what my first question meant and how the Jew answered it."

When the good-natured poritz spoke in that definite manner, the steward knew that no excuse would be accepted. He would have to make the grade. So all the week, in every spare moment, he tried to recall what the poritz had asked the Jew, and what answer the Jew had given that was so amazingly clever. He failed completely. On Saturday he decided that he must wheedle some help from the stonebreaker.

He found the Jew, in neat Sabbath clothes, returning from synagogue. "Here, you—Yekhiel! What's-your-name! Tell me what it was that the noble poritz asked you, when he was kind enough to speak to you the other day. And what was the answer that you gave him?"

"Ah!" the Jew laughed reminiscently. "That was between

the noble poritz and myself. Nobody else would be interested."

"But I'm interested. It was very clever, and I'd like to remember it. But my mind is so taken up. What was the first question he asked you?"

"It's not worth talking about," said the Jew politely. "We exchanged a few remarks, the poritz and I. It's really not worth your trouble."

"But it's worth something to me. How about ten rubles?"

The Jew's expression changed. "I don't talk business on Shabbos," he said firmly.

"Well, I'll come to you this evening," the manager suggested.

"No, why take the trouble? I'll come to you," said Yekhiel.

He came; but he was not interested in ten rubles, or in twenty, or in the gradually mounting sums the manager counted out for him. He laughed off every offer, saying, "But I can't take money for nothing!"

The manager lost his temper. "You impudent Jew! Who are you to refuse me? I could turn you out of your house tomorrow! I could take away your job! What are you but a miserable stone-breaker? And here I am offering you money for a little bit of information."

"Your honor may do as you please about it," the Jew said. "I ask nothing of you."

For hours the one-sided wrangle continued. At last the manager named a large sum. "That's the half of my savings," he announced desperately.

"Then you do need to know it," said Yekhiel, quietly. "This amount I accept. Here is the information:

"The noble poritz asked me, 'Which is more, five or seven?' By that he meant, 'There are only five months of cold weather, and seven months when it's pleasant outdoors. Couldn't you have worked harder in the mild seasons, then you wouldn't have to be breaking stones in this bitter cold?' I replied to the poritz: 'Thirty-two is still more.' Thirty-two is the number of one's teeth. A man has to provide food for himself and his family. To give those teeth enough to chew on, I have to work at my job all seasons of the year."

"Ha! Yes. Very funny," the manager responded sourly.

By the time he saw the poritz after church, however, his mood had mellowed. "Your honor, I remember now the witty remarks you exchanged with the Jew. If I hadn't been figuring how many calves we might expect in spring, I could have repeated your question and answer on the spot. First you asked the Jew . . ." And he recounted what had passed between them.

The poritz laughed appreciatively, all through the recital. "Well, well!" he exclaimed. "So you did understand! I see that I've misjudged you."

"Your honor! You didn't think I was as clever as that good-for-nothing Jew? I must say that's a poor compliment," grumbled the manager.

"Let me make amends, then," said the poritz. "You probably remember the second question I asked him and the way he answered it?"

[167]

The manager hid his annoyance and confusion as best he could. "I'll bring it to mind when I have time, your honor," he mumbled. "I was thinking of the price we'll have to pay for horse-fodder."

"I'll give you time. I won't ask you again until a week from now. Then if you succeed, I'll admit your cleverness, and you can keep your position as my manager."

On the following day the steward hurried to the Jew, where he was working beside the road. "Yekhiel," he said, "you might as well remind me of the second question the poritz asked you, and how you answered him."

"It was only a joke," the Jew replied, pausing for a moment. "A busy man like you needn't bother his head about it."

"All the same, just as a favor, you might tell me. Be a good fellow!"

"It's not worth your while!" The stone-breaker blew on his hands and went back to swinging his pickaxe.

Nothing could alter his reluctance until, on the Saturday evening, the manager offered the remaining half of his savings.

Then the Jew said: "The noble poritz asked me to account for the bad straits I am in, if my house had burned down lately. Now there's a saying among the country people that to give a daughter in marriage is as expensive as having your house burn down. I replied, 'My house has burned down twice, and I expect another fire soon.' In other words, I had married off two of my daughters, and will have to make a wedding feast for my youngest girl this spring. Does that recall it to your memory?"

"Exactly!" the poritz commented when the manager gave him the second answer. "You tell it quite well. You can stay on as my manager. But just to please me, tell me also what was the third question I asked, and why I laughed when he answered it. Don't worry about it. Just tell me a week from today."

For the third time the manager had to give up and ask help of the Jew.

"I don't like to answer," the Jew replied, no longer laughing. "It's better that you shouldn't know."

"By all the saints, what do you want of me!" the manager stormed. "I've given you all my savings. I've nothing left but my position. I can't give you that!"

"You will have to, for you won't be able to keep it. The third question was this: The poritz asked me, 'In how many handfuls could one pluck the rooster?' You, with your conceit and your rough ways, are the rooster. The poritz was asking how long it would take me to strip you of your possessions. I answered that anybody could do it in three handfuls, but I'd undertake to manage it in two. Haven't I succeeded? Can you go back to the poritz and tell him that?"

The manager was groaning and wringing his hands in distress. "What will become of my wife and family? My children will starve if I lose my position, for you've taken from me all my savings!"

"Now you know how other men felt when you lied about

them to the poritz, and took their work away from them and turned them out of their homes. But don't worry. I won't treat you so badly as you have treated us, for a Jew has a merciful heart. Take back your savings and go in peace with them. But I think I'm entitled to your position."

The poritz thought so, too; and from then on, he often enjoyed a lively chat with his new, and popular, manager.

The Miser

A MAN WHO THINKS HIMSELF VERY
RELIGIOUS IS GIVEN A SEVERE SHOCK.

THERE was once a man who by hard striving had raised himself and his family from early poverty to fairly comfortable circumstances. He was now established as a *M'sader K'dushin*—a person qualified to perform the marriage ceremony. Because of his fine appearance and genial, graceful manner his services were preferred in many communities through the countryside.

His success had not freed him, however, from the dread of penury. He kept a strict hand on household expenditures, gave to charity only so much as might spare him criticism, and dressed sufficiently well from motives of shrewdness rather than self-respect or vanity.

When, in middle life, he inherited a good sum of money, which should have freed him from present stinting and from anxiety for the future, it actually had the opposite effect. He made of his strongbox a barrier against misfortune—a haven of safety. From adding to it as much as he could, and counting it up with satisfaction in the growth of the sum, he gradually came to take delight in fingering the coins themselves. He arranged them in piles—gold, silver and copper—stacked them according to value and the year of minting, and as time passed, became unwilling to withdraw even small amounts. To meet expenses by taking money from the coffer, caused him actual suffering.

He postponed giving to the community charities until he forgot his default. Only in cases of pitiful need that suddenly confronted him, giving him no time to consider, was he startled into generosity. Yet he knew himself for a religious person, and thought himself charitable because whenever a couple found it difficult to pay his fee, he would marry them without charge.

Small meannesses crept into his behavior. He would economize by fasting before he went to perform a ceremony, and gorging himself at the wedding feast. Nothing pleased him more than to fill his stomach at another's expense.

His gentle wife was saddened by this growing avarice. At one time, in the busy market, as she tried to stretch the sum he had given her for Sabbath preparations, she overheard some neighbors referring to him. They called him, not Hirschel "Glückenheimer," after the village of his birth, but Hirschel *"Kamzan"*—the "Miser."

She prayed that God would reveal to him the snare into which he had fallen. For she knew that her husband thought of his parsimony as "provision for the future" and "prudent care for his wife and children in later years." She had not the heart to reproach him, nor the words in which to point out his self-deception.

One day a handsome coach-and-four drove up to the house and the personage who entered said to the M'sader K'dushin: "I have come myself to engage your services. I am to be host at a wedding party on my estate, which is almost a day's journey from here. But that need not inconvenience you. If you will be good enough to come with me, you shall remain with us overnight, and I will see to it that you return home in good time. Furthermore, you may name your own fee."

The stranger's attire and the style of his equipage suggested great wealth. Delighted at the prospect, Hirsch Glückenheimer soon joined his patron in the smart coach,

and the gray horses tossed their heads and took the road out of town.

For several hours they drove along level roads, then they mounted to hilly country. The carriage swung and jerked uncontrollably, and despite the well-cushioned seats, the M'sader K'dushin found it a wearisome ride. Darkness fell and the outlook became wilder. They seemed to be plunging through an upland forest. A full moon rose and was visible at moments between tangled branches. But it brought no comfort. It looked down with what seemed to be a grimace.

At length they came out upon a high, meadowlike heath, and Glückenheimer was greatly relieved to see, incongruous amid this wilderness but reassuring, a fine, solid mansion streaming with light and the sound of festivities.

When the host introduced him, the M'sader K'dushin realized that never before had he seen so prepossessing a company. Richly dressed in harmonious colors and perfect taste, they danced with grace and elegance. They conversed in mellifluous tones that blended with the music. They looked at him with gracious kindness and made him welcome.

He was presented to the bride, and for a moment they were left together. She came closer to him and said: "All present here are spirits. I alone am a mortal like yourself. As you value your soul, accept no gift or fee. Do not eat or drink in this house!"

A moment later she was smiling as the bridegroom took her hand and led her to join a minuet.

[174]

Glückenheimer found a seat and sank into it. He felt a chill on his skin, as if the air had turned to ice. Looking about him, he understood the charm of that first impression. Here was no clumsiness, no obesity, no harshness, no screeching laughter, no fumbling, feeble age, as would surely figure at any mortal wedding. Their perfection threatened him. He felt himself weak and in their power.

But he was not alone for long. The host sought him out and insisted that he take some refreshment after his tiring journey.

Sternly—and warily—the M'sader K'dushin refused. When they pressed him, he excused himself with the plea that it was his custom to fast for twenty-four hours before the ceremony, so that his prayers for the future happiness of the young couple might be more acceptable.

Everybody praised his wholeheartedness; and the host, seeing that he would not be persuaded to break his fast, suggested he might wish to retire.

Glückenheimer gratefully assented. He was brought to a luxurious chamber, where he lay down on a cloud-soft bed and drew the curtains around him. It was a strange night. He slept, but woke frequently, always with the feeling that some elusive presence was slipping beyond his field of vision, or that he had failed to hear a message of importance, or that a song had ceased the very moment of his awakening.

In the morning his ordeal continued. He was seated with the guests of honor at an elaborate breakfast, lasting for hours. Fresh dainties were brought to the table continuously, and the host never gave up trying to persuade him to taste this or that delicacy, or give his opinion of some special wine. Complimentary speeches, songs to the guitar, and choral interludes lengthened out the meal. Pale and inwardly wretched, Glückenheimer refused to be tempted. The meal finally ended and the guests stood up for the ceremony. When it came to pronouncing the blessing on wine, the M'sader K'dushin merely touched his lips to the sacramental winecup, allowing no drop to enter them.

At last he was free to leave, amid thanks and compliments from the guests. "Now let's see if we can repay you for your great kindness," said the host. "Come with me."

They entered a room at the contents of which Glückenheimer's face brightened and his eyes gleamed. Piles of silver lay at the foot of pillars festooned with silver wreaths and garlands. Silver vases brimmed over with coin, silver trays held yet more objects of sterling silver. It was such wealth as he could not have anticipated.

"Take as much as you wish," said his companion, casually.

Glückenheimer, despite a tug at his heart, replied "Thank you for your liberality. But . . . you need not pay me. Your gratitude is enough."

"I see, such stuff as this does not appeal to you," the host responded. "Very well! We have something here that may be more to your taste." And he led the M'sader K'dushin into a chamber yet more dazzling.

The pillars were of red gold. The floor was tessellated in squares of green and yellow gold. Piles of newly minted coins, boxes of antique money, bowls and vessels exquisitely chased and figured and embossed so that the art of their craftsmanship multiplied manyfold the value of the metal, drew his fascinated gaze from one marvel to another.

"Ah, perhaps the weight concerns you?" said his host. "Have no fear of that. We shall undertake to bring it to you. You have only to choose."

Faintness welled up in Glückenheimer. He closed his eyes against the maddening sight. "No. Again I must protest that you owe me nothing," he sighed.

"This, too, is beneath you, I see. Pardon me for having misjudged you."

They entered a third room. The walls were hung with dark velvet, the floor carpeted in gray. Bowls of glowing gems stood on pedestals of alabaster. Rubies from rose pink to blood red; deep green emeralds, sapphires, diamonds like white fire, pearls of all colors and magnificent size.

But here the temptation was already less. Never had Glückenheimer imagined such splendor, and it formed no part of his dreams. It was unreal to him. He had little difficulty in saying, "No, I thank you. This is more than I have earned and I want none of it. Pray, let me return home."

The face of his host showed a grim relief. He opened another door and with his hand on Glückenheimer's shoulder led him through. This was a small, bare room with walls of whitewashed brick. Hundreds of keys were displayed hanging from plain iron hooks. Among them Glückenheimer recognized, with a last flare of astonishment, the key to his own strongbox.

His companion gave it to him, saying: "Whenever a

coffer is made, two keys are fashioned for it. One is the owner's key. The other is God's. If God's key is not used, the owner will find it harder and harder to take money from the box. He will open it only to add more and more to the hoard; and, eventually, his soul will be locked up in it.

"We are spirits who serve the Lord. Remember what has been revealed to you. Take God's key, and use it."

A door on the opposite side of the little room swung open. Glückenheimer stepped through it, and found himself in his study, at home.

He burst into thanksgiving at his escape. Then he took from the box one-tenth—the Biblical tithe—of all it contained, and humbly brought it to the community chest.

When the Shofar
Was Silent

RABBI ELIJAH of Vilna, honored by Talmudic students of his time with the rare title of *Gaon,* or "Excellent," held a peculiar place in the community.

He would accept no official post. Independently, near the monumental Great Synagogue, he opened another house of prayer, a small one, himself choosing those who were to make up its congregation. He selected, too, scholars who valued wide and general learning, to join him in his house of study. Yet so admirable was his tact, and so vital his philosophy, that his free action created no resentment or jealousy but rather a sense of enlightenment. He became, without his own volition, a spokesman and a leader of his people.

And much they needed his steadying faith. To the

[179]

Jews of Vilna, the last ten years of the eighteenth century opened in a cloud of dark prevision. Poland had already been twice rent asunder by her neighbors. The Grand Duchy of Lithuania, with their own Vilna, was coveted by Catherine II of Russia. It was still a part of Poland, but who knew what changes the coming year might bring?

Thus the congregation gathering in the Gaon's synagogue on the eve of Rosh Ha-Shanah, the Jewish New Year, had many anxieties in mind. They hoped that their prayers on this day, when the Book of Judgment is opened in Heaven, and each person's record is read, and each fate decided for the next twelve months, would win God's approval of themselves and the community. They awaited the shofar blasts, symbolic of the awakened conscience, that were to embarrass Satan, the Accuser. With joy they saw that the Gaon himself was to sound the primitive ram's horn.

They watched the tall, erect figure coming forward to the reading desk. He took up the shofar, and with a solemn, prayerful expression he set it to his lips.

They waited for the long, harsh "wailing cry" of the horn to burst forth. They waited, but no sound came. The reader called for a "trembling" blast, hoping it might prove easier. Again the Gaon tried, but again with no success. Minute after minute passed in anxious silence, as he wondered miserably, how was it that when he had sounded the shofar in practice on the days before the festival, everything had gone well? And now, in the great moment, he was failing! What could it mean?

[180]

For Rabbi Elijah it was a harrowing experience. However, he did not keep his listeners waiting longer, but gave the shofar to the cantor, asking him to sound it. The cantor, perhaps unnerved by the Gaon's failure, also failed to produce a note.

The horn was handed to the *dayan,* the judge next in rank to the rabbi. He, too, did no better. After him, the president of the synagogue, the treasurer, and even the *shammas* tried. Not one of them, try as he might, could sound the shofar.

The worshipers were shaken by the long suspense. The failure of the ram's horn seemed a dismaying omen.

At last, a poor and simple person from the back benches, volunteered to try. He came to the reading desk, took the shofar in hand, and making hardly an effort, blew it powerfully. With glad relief the congregation listened to the inspiring sounds:

"*T'kioh!*"—One long wailing blast.

"*T'ruoh!*"—Three trembling cries.

"*Shevorim!*"—Six short staccato notes.

Then t'kioh, t'ruoh, and shevorim, in varying order, just as the reader dictated. A breath of thankfulness passed through the hearers, and the prayers were resumed.

"Who is the man that blew the shofar?" the Gaon asked, when the service was over.

"Mosheh Levner is his name, Rabbi," he was told. "A wagoner. A simple Jew without learning, whom you yourself invited to join the synagogue, because of his many deeds of neighborliness to those about him."

"Ah. I remember," said the rabbi, and spoke no more on the subject.

But from that day on, his manner changed. He who had always taught gladness of heart—who maintained that "Man ought to feel cheered by the privilege of serving God and occupying himself with the divine commandments—" he fell into a deep sadness. He became distressingly quiet and humble. His pupils and colleagues were touched. No longer did he jest with them, in high spirits, over the subtle points of wisdom in the Law. No longer did he sing at his prayers, in exuberant fervor. He prayed in whispers.

It followed that he became physically ill. However, instead of a physician to cure him, he sent for the learned and witty preacher, Jacob of Dubno.

"Rabbi, you have no reason to be downcast," said the *Dubner Maggid*. "What fear has crept into your heart? You torment yourself about a matter of small account!"

"No," the Gaon murmured. "There must be a serious fault in my character, a blemish, by reason of which I was thought unworthy to sound the shofar. I am trying to search for it and correct it."

"Let me tell you a story," said the Maggid, in his rich, cheerful voice. "There was once a king to whom a remarkable gem had been presented. It was so handsome a stone that few in the whole world could compare with it. The King wished to have it set in a jeweled collar, which he would wear at the celebration of his jubilee. But for this purpose, it must be pierced through the exact center.

"He sent for the court jeweler, who exclaimed: 'What a magnificent diamond! A most rare and valuable stone! How does His Majesty wish it set?'

"When the King explained what he wanted, the jeweler remarked, half-jestingly: 'One must have a steady hand for such a task. I should not like to make a slip!'

" 'You had better not,' the King said brusquely. 'Your life will pay for it, if you injure one of the facets. It will be instant death for you!'

"The jeweler bowed low and returned the gem to its case. 'Your Majesty, I am getting older,' he sighed. 'I don't feel able to undertake this distinguished task. I pray you to excuse me.'

" 'But if you succeed,' the King added, 'we shall double your yearly salary and add a thousand dinars beside.'

" 'It is most gracious of Your Majesty,' the jeweler said, 'but allow me to retire.' And he bowed his way out.

"The King sent for the best diamond merchant in his capital city and offered the post of court jeweler to the craftsman who should bore a hole through the center of the diamond. The merchant was willing to undertake it himself, but as the King talked on, and mentioned the penalty for a slip in cutting the stone, he, too, changed his mind about it and declined to make the attempt.

"Then the King sent invitations to foreign jewelers, offering great sums of money. But no one could be found who would risk his life in so delicate a performance.

"At last, the prime minister advised him: 'Your Majesty, send for an ordinary diamond cutter, one who is experienced and skillful with his tools. Tell him nothing about the value of the gem, or how serious it will be if he fails to pierce it flawlessly.'

"The King did as suggested. The craftsman turned the gem about admiringly, weighed it in his hands, selected a tool—and began. In a very short time the gem was correctly pierced. Nothing went wrong, and the workman was rewarded."

The Gaon looked up, a smile forming on his lips.

"You see, Rabbi," his visitor continued, "it was the same in your case. You, who tremble for our people, and know the dangers we face; you, who can weigh the facts, and doubt that Russian Tsardom will be any kinder to us than the tolerant Kings of Poland—when you came with such cares on your mind, and fully realizing the significance of the ceremony, and feeling that you must perform it perfectly, why, you became so nervous that your throat contracted, your breath was cut off, and you could not utter a sound. Whereas the simple wagoner, who offered to try because his good heart ached for your embarrassment, *he* was able to succeed!"

The Gaon laughed heartily and his malaise left him.

Rabbi Hayim
and the Emperor

NAPOLEON SEEKS A PRESAGE FROM AN OLD RABBI.

IN the Russian town of Volozhin lived Rabbi
Hayim, head of an academy he had founded to carry on
the teaching of his master, the Vilner Gaon. Rabbi Hayim
himself, incidentally, acquired a great reputation for general
wisdom and prescience. In this connection a tale is still
remembered about his meeting with Napoleon Bonaparte,
Emperor of the French.

Napoleon had just begun his invasion. He had barely
penetrated the Pale—the strip of land where Jews were
allowed to settle—when he and his army encamped one
night near Volozhin.

Immediately the townspeople fled. They hid in caves
and forest, waiting for the enemy to pass on. Only one
person dared to remain and meet the conqueror. French
officers, as their men ransacked the storehouses for food,

came upon Rabbi Hayim, alone in the academy, calmly proceeding with his studies. He was taken at once before Napoleon.

"Where are the other townspeople?" Bonaparte asked him.

"Hiding from you," the old man said.

"Where?"

"If I had gone with them, I might be able to answer. As it is, I am here." He shrugged.

Napoleon dismissed his adjutants. Alone with the Rabbi, the Emperor regarded him silently for some moments.

Then speech burst from him. "I am told that you are very wise, and that you can even foretell the future. Tell me, then, shall I win this war or not? Shall I be successful as heretofore, or will my enemies get the better of me in the end?"

The rabbi responded with a faint smile and a steady silence.

"Come, conceal nothing from me. Do not fear to tell me the truth."

"Is the Emperor God, that I should fear him?" said the rabbi. "If you wish it, however, I shall tell you what I foresee. But first, listen to a story:

"Once, in a faraway country, on a high, wide tableland, a prince was driving his carriage drawn by three strong and beautiful horses. Proudly he sat behind his fiery steeds, which were swift as forest deer. Suddenly, one of the horses stumbled and fell. The others took fright, turned off

the path and plunged into a ditch that ran beside the road.

"The Prince tried to get them up, but all the lashings of his whip, and all his angry commands were in vain. The horses lay in the ditch, and could neither find their own footing nor pull the carriage out. The Prince jumped from his seat at last, and looked around for help.

"He saw a farmer's wagon hurrying towards him; but his call for help was sharply broken off, for the farmer's three bony and shrunken horses also lost their footing and fell in the ditch, pulling their master and his wagon after them.

"Immediately, however, the farmer climbed down from his wagon, grasped the reins of the right-hand horse, and struck the middle one with his whip. Before the Prince could count three, the farmer's team had struggled up from the ditch and the wagon was on the road again, ready to go on its way.

"The Prince, in surprise, called out to the farmer: 'How was that? Can you tell me why it is that your horses got out of the ditch at the first stroke of your whip, and mine have not moved, even after many beatings? Anyone can see, with all respect to you, that my horses are of better breed and training than yours?'

" 'That is true,' said the farmer. 'But tell me, where did you buy your animals?'

" 'Oh, my horses,' said the Prince, 'were brought to me from different lands. They cost thousands of gold pieces. This one—' the Prince pointed to the left-hand horse—

'is from Arabia. The middle one is of famous Spanish stock, and the one on the right was bred in Italy.'

" 'Well,' said the farmer, 'that is the cause of your trouble. They are beautiful horses, no mistake, and it must be fine to have so much money that you can pay for the best from each country. But that has its dangers, too. Now, my horses are all of one stock. This in the middle is the mother, and the other two are her daughters. When my whip touches the mother, all three feel the pain. You yourself saw how quickly they scrambled out of the ditch at the very first flick of my whip. The outer ones were afraid that I might hurt their mother, as well as themselves. But your horses felt no pity for each other's pain.'

"Now, my lord the Emperor," Rabbi Hayim continued, "what happened to that Prince, will also happen to you. It is true that you are a great general, and that your army is brave and well trained and mighty as the sea. But there are among you, beside the French, many German and Italian divisions, as well as soldiers of fortune from many different lands. It is not for your sake that they have joined your army, but for their own profit. On the other hand, the soldiers of the Russian army are all sons of one mother— the Russian people. And if you fight against her, all her sons will rush as one man to save her from you.

"And as for you, O great Napoleon, who can tell whether even you will survive?"

Saddened and thoughtful, the Emperor looked up at the white-bearded Jew and gave orders that he be released and conducted back to his place in safety.

That very day Napoleon's army struck camp and passed on to its fate. And when the people of Volozhin returned to their homes, they found them exactly as they had left them, unentered, the family treasures untouched. For this the townspeople gave the credit to Rabbi Hayim, and the respect he inspired even in the enemy.

The Poor Man's Fortune

THERE IS A VERSE IN THE BOOK
OF PSALMS THAT GUIDED HIM.

THIS is the story of a poor man with four little children whom he had to bring up by himself. Until the death of his wife a few months after the youngest was born, he had never felt the sharpness of poverty. For he had his skill as a shoemaker, and his own small shop, and contentment in the little rooms behind his store.

But with the loss of his wife, everything changed for the worse. He tried to give his children proper care while keeping up with his work. The work fell behind; and then fell off. A new anxiety took its place. After a long, harassing struggle, he was forced to give up the little business he had once so proudly achieved.

He moved with his children to a miserable attic, and he went out looking for work in other men's cobbler shops.

But when he did find work, it lasted no more than a few days. He continued his search for steady employment, meanwhile gladly doing any jobs that came his way.

He would go home every few hours to feed the children on whatever he could provide. Then he went out again to look for work.

One evening, he actually had no food to give the little ones. They went hungry to bed.

The poor man had eaten nothing that day. With a great sigh, he sat down to study the holy books, from which he had always drawn comfort and encouragement. Turning the pages of the Book of Psalms, his eye fell upon the verse:

> I have been young, and now am old;
> Yet have I not seen the righteous forsaken,
> Nor his seed begging bread.

"How can this be?" he cried. "All my life I have tried to do right. I worked hard. I did my best. I have helped others who needed help. Master of the Universe, You who gave me my children! Why am I unable to provide for them?"

He became sadder still. "What has become of me, that I question God's will?" His heart shook within him. He felt a dread loneliness. "Have I lost my faith in God?" he murmured.

Then a new thought occurred to him. "I will go to see the rabbi, early in the morning, even before I look for work. I will ask him to explain the meaning of this verse. He will help me to understand and abide by God's will."

Comforted by this decision, he lay down and slept uncommonly well.

On the very day of the poor man's crisis, the rabbi was visited by a wealthy merchant from a neighboring town. They drank tea together and asked for news of local happenings. Then the visitor sat back and with a benign, reflective expression, said:

"Rabbi, I have a peculiar matter to discuss with you. As you see, I am a man of means. God has blessed me with prosperity and many good gifts. Only one trouble He laid upon me. I am childless except for one girl. She is sweet, and clever, and good—a jewel! Everything that parents can wish, except that she is only one.

"But we thanked God for her, and cherished her, and brought her up as a fine Jewish daughter.

"Imagine our grief when, a year ago, she fell ill—dangerously ill—and nothing could be done to cure her. I sent for a famous doctor. We watched by her, day and night. But for all our striving, she faded away. Before our eyes, she was dying.

"We had only one recourse left. My wife ran through the streets to the synagogue, and I, like a madman, after her. She burst in, and the worshipers made way. She tore open the doors of the Ark of Holiness, and flung herself down before the Torah scrolls, and cried to God beseeching Him to spare our only one.

"And I, in that moment, I vowed that whatever sum I might acquire in the whole year, beyond my bare necessities,

we would give to God, for community needs and for the poor.

"And, do you know, Rabbi, our treasure recovered. She is well today, thank God, and great is our satisfaction. As for my vow, never have I had a more prosperous year than this one. The sum that came to me above what I need, is so great that I feel it must be distributed by one who can do most good with it. You know the community and its needs. I have brought it to you."

Naming the amount it contained, the merchant set a bag of gold on the table.

"That is too great a sum for me to handle!" the rabbi exclaimed. "I cannot accept the responsibility. But you are a man of affairs. It is your gift and your vow. Distribute it yourself."

"But I do not wish to be known as the giver. It must be given for the glory of God."

"Very well, then," the rabbi suggested. "Give me the names of any worthy poor persons of your acquaintance, and I will portion it out among them."

"You know the people better than I do," said the merchant. "You know their needs. I will be satisfied with your decision, whatever it be."

The rabbi thought a while. "Let us leave the decision to God," he said at length. "I shall give the whole sum to the first poor man who crosses my threshold tomorrow."

Soon after daybreak, a shabby person knocked humbly on the door and was admitted. The rabbi recognized the bony, patient face and eager eyes.

"*Barukh ha-Bah!*" he cried. "Blessed be he who comes . . . in the name of the Lord!" He seated the newcomer and made him welcome. And before the poor man could speak a word, the rabbi told him the merchant's story and produced the bag of gold.

"Take it, my son," he said. "It is all yours. Find a good servant to care for your children. Give them a comfortable home again. Open a new business. Everything will go well with you!"

Dizzy with joy and exhausted from the long struggle, the listener sat still a while. Then he said "Rabbi, Rabbi, you have answered my question before I could ask it!"

```
/\/\/\/\/\/\/\/\/\/\/\/\/\/\/\/\/\/\/\/\/\/\/\/\/\/\/\
```

His Father's
Promise

```
\/\/\/\/\/\/\/\/\/\/\/\/\/\/\/\/\/\/\/\/\/\/\/\/\/\/\
```

A FAMILY REUNION AND WHAT THE
SUCCESSFUL SON FOUND THERE.

A lumber merchant living in a village of eastern Europe had three sons. They were intelligent, vigorous young men of whom any father might be proud. The youngest chose to stay at home and learn the father's trade, but the two older sons felt they would do better in a large town, where one sees more of what goes on in the world.

So the father gave each of them a sum sufficient to start him in business, and they left for the same big city.

Once there, they met with different fortunes. The older brother throve. He had good abilities and he worked hard. He made the most of every chance. He knew how to get on with people and also, perhaps, how to use them for his own advantage. Within a few years of his arrival in the city, he

[197]

married into a wealthy family and was able to enlarge his business.

The younger brother, though he was equally capable and worked just as hard, met with a different fate. Perhaps because he could not push himself everywhere, or did not feel so certain that whatever he wished was right, this young man made little progress. The money with which he had started out dwindled instead of increasing. Luck never favored him. Advice and even help from his brother during the first year or so, did nothing to brighten his days. He became discouraged, and fearing to be thought of as a *shlemihl,* he ceased to visit his brother and plodded along in his own drudging way.

The older one, as if dropping a load from his shoulders, was willing on the whole to forget him.

Time went by. One day the prosperous brother received a particularly pleasant letter from home. The youngest son was to be married, and the father wrote requesting that his two other sons come home for the wedding.

"Come and bring your family," the letter ran. "It will give me great joy. Bring your brother with you, too. Do not hesitate on account of the expense, my son. I will gladly refund all that you spend in fulfilling the commandment to honor your father!"

From then on until the time of departure, the eldest son was occupied with his preparations. He and his wife and children were measured for new clothes and new shoes. He made careful plans for the conduct of his business during his absence. He engaged a well-appointed coach for the journey, and sent messengers ahead to reserve quarters at the finest inns.

In the course of the fittings and the packing, he sent word for his brother to come and see him. When the brother failed to appear, he gave it little thought. We can pick him up on the way, he told himself. After all, he's alone. And what he's doing isn't so important that he can't leave it.

When the eldest brother and his family were all dressed up in the new traveling outfits and had taken their places in the coach, they drove to the younger one's lodging.

"Why didn't you come to me? Why must everything be left until the last minute?" the older one demanded.

"Why was it so important for you to see me, all of a sudden?" the younger brother retorted. "For years you've shown no interest in me. Why should I dance attendance, at a word from you?"

The older one controlled himself. "Get in, and I'll tell you about it," he said. "We have a *simhah*—"

"A simhah? Then I'll change to my Sabbath suit."

The Sabbath suit was neat, but care and mending could not hide the shine at the seams or the fraying of button-holes. It was the same that he had brought from home; only it hung on him now, for he had grown thinner. And the polishing he had given his shoes made the patches on them more noticeable. As he climbed into the coach, the older brother exchanged a glance of distaste with his wife. She shrugged. What could one make of such a *shlimmazzel?*

The coach arrived in splendid style. As it dashed along the town's one street to the lumber merchant's home, all the householders turned out to see it. By village custom, everybody had been invited to the wedding; so they all had a right to be interested in the guests.

—Who was this portly, fine-looking Jew, with the attractive wife so fashionably dressed, and the handsome, city-bred children?

—Who *should* he be, but the son, of course, of the richest man in town?

Everyone was eager to claim acquaintance or be introduced, and—if allowed—to remain near the newcomers and share in their celebrity.

At the marriage ceremony, all eyes followed these important guests in their silks and satins, to a place of honor beside the *huppah*. The bridegroom's relatives never tired of explaining who they were to the relatives of the bride.

Nobody paid much attention to the younger brother. Indeed, he did not mingle in the festivities but stood aside, as an onlooker. At the wedding feast he was seated at table with the bride and groom, not far from his father. But while others made speeches, told stories and took part in discussions, he remained quiet, as if content to be passed over. If anyone happened to ask about him, the relatives described him as a "member of the family."

So it went, during a week of rejoicing and celebrations. After the second Sabbath in the old home, the eldest son said: "This has been a happy visit, Father, and I would

7071

Williston Park Public Library

gladly stay longer. But, you know, my business requires
that I return. We must make ready to go."

The father nodded graciously. "Go in health, my son!"

But he said nothing of his promise to pay the expenses
of the journey. Apparently, he had forgotten all about it.

To remind him, the son made a careful, itemized list
of all that he had laid out. The cost of the new clothes,
the hire of the coach, the several changes of horses, overnight lodging at the inns, money spent for food along the
way. It amounted to quite a large sum. He presented it
to the old man shortly before taking leave.

"Remember, Father, how you promised to repay the
expenses of our visit to you? Here's the account."

His father studied the paper. "No, my son," he replied
at length. "I made no such promise."

His memory is failing, the son told himself. Respectfully, with a little smile, he took the letter of invitation from
his pocket. "Here it is, Father. In your own handwriting."

Again the father was silent for some time. He cleared
his throat, then he began to speak.

"You misunderstood what I wrote you, my son. Read
again, and you will see what I said. I said I would gladly
repay all that you spent in fulfilling the commandment
to honor your father.

"That is what you have *not* done. Had you really wished
to honor me, you would have been considerate of your
brother. You would have taken pains to see that he made a
good appearance. He, too, is my son. Don't you think it
hurt me to see him sitting alone, or among the old people

who knew him as a child? I know his pride. He would not mingle with the younger guests for fear of drawing attention to his poverty and shaming the rest of us. If you had wished to spare me pain, you would have made him feel welcome, and not neglected him as if unworthy of notice. Then I should have been only too happy to keep my promise!

"But now, my son, much as I love you, I must repeat that whatever you have done, your object was not to honor your father.

"It was yourself whom you honored. Not me."

It is much the same, when we undertake to serve God, said the *Dubner Maggid* in telling this story. We show a true desire to honor Him, only if we love and care for our fellow-men.

The Word of a Schnorrer

AN ENCOUNTER BETWEEN A BEGGAR AND
THE FATHER OF THE ROTHSCHILDS.

"SCHNORRER" may be translated "beggar,"
but the English word will convey only a fraction of the
true meaning. In essence, a schnorrer was a man who took
pride in his skill—a professional, not necessarily a trickster.
He felt justified in his occupation not only by need, but
by what he construed as a mission. The Talmud stated
that the rich were able, by beneficence and charity, to
reconcile the poor with God's will. The schnorrer, with
varying degrees of finesse, took upon himself to remind the
wealthy of this privilege.

A certain anecdote sheds the best light on the subject.
Baron Rothschild, known for his generous gifts to those
in need, was so busy one day that he shut himself in his
library and told the servants that he was not to be disturbed
on any account.

[203]

A schnorrer presented himself at the front door and asked to see the Baron. The footman replied: "The Baron sees nobody today. Come tomorrow."

"But this matter can't wait! I *must* see him!" said the visitor, and pushed past the servant into the house. Another footman stopped him at the staircase. "I must see the Baron. It's a matter of life and death!" the schnorrer exclaimed and made his way upstairs. A third manservant stood guard before the library door.

"I know the Baron's in there!" cried the schnorrer. "Don't try to keep me out! The Baron himself would blame you—"

By this time the two downstairs servants had caught up with the intruder and the three footmen together tried to remove him; but the schnorrer succeeded in bursting open the door and getting inside. The Baron looked up from his desk, much annoyed.

"Herr Baron, this is an emergency! Your good heart will tell you that you must help me!"

"Must I, indeed?" the Baron replied hotly. "What do you think you'll accomplish by breaking in when I expressly ordered that I was not to be disturbed!"

The man drew himself erect. "Baron Rothschild," he said with dignity, "*schnorring* I understand better than you."

So much for the schnorrer's professional pride and Baron Rothschild's experience with it. A still stranger encounter figures in the family annals. Meyer Amschel, the father of the Rothschilds and the founder of their fortunes, is the target of this one. For he had established their practice of personal philanthropy, and was often troubled by over-insistent schnorrers.

One, in particular, he remembered. This was a Polish Jew, very ragged and shrewd-looking, who would not leave though repeatedly advised by the servants to come the following day. "Herr Amschel cannot see you now," they said.

"But what harm will it do if I see *him*? Let me come in. I will speak *one word* to Reb Amschel, and then go."

"Impossible. Herr Amschel must not be disturbed."

"Disturbed? *I* won't disturb him." The schnorrer seemed more shocked than they were, at the mere possibility. "I will say *one word*, and then leave."

"But we are to admit nobody."

"I'm not just anybody. I'm different. I will say one word, and I will come out at once."

The two servants looked at each other, beginning to weaken. They knew their master loved a joke, and wryly enjoyed the tricks of such witty nuisances, even when employed against himself. "Very well," they said at length, "but remember your promise. Say only one word."

The man nodded vigorously, as if already renouncing speech. He entered Meyer Amschel's office and bowed low. "*Gemorah!*" he said, and marched out.

The banker looked up in surprise and saw the schnorrer turning tail. What did the man mean by "Gemorah"?— And why had he, evidently a beggar, gone away so swiftly? Curious and faintly amused, he rang for the servants.

"Is the man who came in and said—something—a word

I didn't understand—is he still here? Then bring him in."

They went to call the schnorrer. "Herr Amschel has sent for you," they said. "Go in."

"No. No." said the beggar, repudiating the temptation with raised shoulders and a fervent shaking of his head. "I promised I would speak only one word. You allowed it. I thank you. But I will not disturb him."

"Herr Amschel himself wishes to see you."

"No. Not even for Reb Amschel will I break my promise to you."

"But *we* ask you, and Herr Amschel wants to talk to you. So come in."

The schnorrer shrugged as if casting his responsibilities on the servants, and went back with them into Amschel's presence.

"What did you mean by that word?" the banker asked him.

The Polish Jew put one hand on his lips and raised the other piously to show that, at all costs, he would be true to his agreement.

"But you may speak now," Amschel assured him. Again the man frowned, turning his head aside, and with both hands extended, palms forward, pushed away the thought of such bad faith.

"But I myself release you from your promise," Meyer Amschel insisted. "Come. You may speak."

"Gemorah!" the schnorrer said.

"Yes. And what does it mean?"

"Ge—*Mo*—*R*—*A!* Good *Morning*, Reb Amschel."

"Good morning to *you!*" said Amschel amiably. "But surely you didn't come in only to greet me. Stay a moment. Tell me what you want."

"Gemorah!" was the answer.

"Yes, what else does it mean?"

"Give *Mo*ney, Reb Amschel!"

The banker laughed and gave his visitor five gulden.

The schnorrer bowed his thanks and repeated: "Gemorah!" Once again he made for the door, but again Amschel stopped him. "Come, what else is in that word? Speak up!"

"Give *Mo*re, Reb Amschel!" And this time, he was gone.

Laughing again, Amschel gave a servant ten gulden and sent him after the peculiar mendicant. Two minutes later, the schnorrer returned, with a beaming face.

"Gemorah!" he said warmly.

"What is it now?"

"Good *Ma*n, Reb Amschel!" he murmured, and bowed himself out.

The Rabbi Was Late for Kol Nidrei

ON THE HOLIEST NIGHT OF THE JEWISH YEAR—
'THE EVE OF THE DAY OF ATONEMENT—THE RABBI
WAS ABSENT FROM SYNAGOGUE. WHY?

THE fast from sunset to sunset had begun and the synagogue was crowded for the opening service of the Day of Atonement. In this small town of the Russian Pale —the only district in which ordinary Jews were allowed to live—all were neighbors. Every person was known to the other members of the congregation. All were present—save one. The rabbi had not yet arrived.

The cantor stood ready to chant the *Kol Nidrei*—the prayer asking forgiveness for impulsive vows, broken because they proved too hard to carry out. The choir clustered behind him. They watched the empty space in front of the reading desk with astonished eyes.

The uneasy hush was broken only by rustling and fid-

geting as the realization spread among the worshipers. The
rabbi was late.

But how could that be? He was never late for any service,
much less could he be late for this, the most important
service of the year!

Then they began to worry. The rabbi was an old man.
Perhaps illness had detained him. Perhaps he had fainted.
The *shammas* was sent to look for him.

The shammas hurried to the rabbi's house, but found it
locked. Peering anxiously in at the windows, he saw no
one. By the flickering light of the memorial candles, everything seemed to be in order. More perplexed than ever, he
returned to the synagogue.

The question had grown to a mystery. Where had the
rabbi gone? Wild ideas arose in some minds. Only one
thing was certain. They would not begin the service without
him.

Now the rabbi had set out for the synagogue in good
time. He would have arrived well before the congregation
assembled, except that, passing a small, shabby house at
the roadside, he heard a baby crying. And above the infant's
shrieks, a little girl's voice exclaimed in desperation: "Oh,
what shall I do? I can't stop him. What shall I do?"

The old rabbi thought of the synagogue and the Yom
Kippur service shortly to begin. He must not delay— Yet
how could he pass by and not help, where children seemed
to be grieving?

He pushed open the door. A little girl of ten, with long
braids and reddened eyes, was walking to and fro, trying

to quiet the screaming baby in her arms. His face was red and his fists tightly clenched. He wriggled, in pain, or anger, so that she could hardly hold him.

The rabbi quickly entered. "Where's your mother, little girl?" he asked.

"She's gone to synagogue, with Father. I was taking care of my baby brother; but now, he's crying so much I'm afraid he'll hurt himself, and I don't know what to do."

"Leave him with me, little daughter," the rabbi said, as he took off his coat. "Go, call your mother."

The old man gathered the squirming infant firmly in his arms and held him up against one shoulder, meanwhile stroking and patting his back, to relieve stomach pains.

Gradually the crying grew less. The rabbi sat down with the child on his lap, and clicking his tongue, made funny faces. The baby stopped crying to stare at him. With tears still hanging on its lashes, it reached out for the long white beard, took hold with the little fists, and pulled. The rabbi chuckled and rode the baby on his knee.

Suddenly, the infant screwed up its face again, and wept for want of its mother. The rabbi rose and walked to and fro with it, singing melodies from the service. Once in a while, he tossed the baby up towards the ceiling, which delighted it very much.

At length it seemed to become drowsy. The rabbi held it close, swaying backward and forward, intoning the chant: "Let us forgive the entire congregation of Israel."

When the troubled mother returned home, she found the

old man, dressed in his white *kittel*, still rocking the baby in his arms, where it had fallen asleep.

"Rabbi!" she cried, "so this is why you're late! Oh, how can I thank you!"

Smiling, he gave her the baby and hurried to the synagogue.

He found the congregation watching the doorway as one man. The president and treasurer anxiously escorted him to the reading desk. But the rabbi spoke to them placidly, as though nothing unusual had occurred.

"It is right that we grown-up people, on this day of repentance, should weep and beat our breasts, when we think of our sins. But I could not bear to see little children crying their hearts out, and weeping when they haven't sinned at all."

GLOSSARY

Abba
: Aramaic, meaning "father." In general a title of pre-eminence before the name of a distinguished scholar. In Abbayé's case, it was also an affectionate nickname, meaning "Little Father."

Agunah
: Hebrew. A woman, presumably a widow, who has no proof of her husband's death.

Altneuschule
: German for the "Old-New Synagogue." The oldest synagogue in Prague, dating perhaps from the eleventh century, though the present building more probably was erected in the fourteenth.

bas
: Hebrew for "daughter" or "daughter of."

ben
: Hebrew for "son" or "son of."

"Barukh ha-Bah b'shem Adonai"
: Hebrew. "Blessed be he who comes in the name of the Lord!" The greeting by the priests in ancient Jerusalem, to pilgrims arriving at the Temple. Popularly, "Barukh ha-Bah! . . ." ("Blessed be he who comes . . . !") is employed as a welcome to a newly arrived friend or acquaintance.

Dayan
: Hebrew for "judge." The judge of a rabbinical court. He is qualified, as all rabbis are not, to judge in money matters and problems of civil law.

Dybbuk
: Pronounced "dib-book." Hebrew, meaning "attachment." In cabalistic folklore, the soul of a sinner which, after death, "takes possession" of a living person.

E'mes
: Hebrew for "truth." An attribute of God, and one of His wonder-working names.

[215]

Gaon   Hebrew for "excellent." The title very
                rarely conferred, and then only by the
                common agreement of Talmudic scholars,
                on the one most distinguished among them.

Ghetto   Italian for a Jewish quarter, originally.
                Now taken as meaning any segregated
                district.

Golem   Hebrew, meaning "a shapeless mass." In
                folklore, a creature, incomplete but living,
                formed through cabalistic rites for a special,
                sanctified purpose.

Haham   Hebrew for "wise." The title of a rabbi
                among the *Sephardim,* or Spanish and
                Portuguese Jews.

Havdalah   Hebrew for "distinction" in the sense of
                "separation." The ceremony at sundown
                that ends the Sabbath.

Huppah   Hebrew for "canopy," erected for the
                marriage ceremony.

ibn   Arabic, meaning "the son of."

Judengasse   German for "the Jews' street," or Jewish
                quarter.

Kamzan   Hebrew for "miser."

Kittel   Yiddish. A white garment worn as a
                shroud. Because of the solemnity of the
                Day of Atonement, it was the custom of
                the rabbi, the cantor, and others officiating,
                besides individuals among the worshipers,
                to wear the kittel at the services.

Kohen   Hebrew meaning "priest." Plural, "Ko-
                hanim." The Kohanim were the first rank
                of the ancient priesthood. They were
                descended directly from the family of
                Aaron, the first high priest.

"Kol Nidrei"	Hebrew, meaning "All the vows." The opening prayer of the service on Yom Kipper Eve, from which it is called "Kol Nidrei Night."
Levite	A descendant from the Tribe of Levi, the men of which in ancient times served as the lesser rank of the priesthood, in Temple ritual and as musicians and teachers.
Maggid	Hebrew meaning "preacher." The Dubner Maggid was the celebrated preacher coming originally from the town of Dubno.
Matzoh	Unleavened bread, rolled into flat cakes. The only bread eaten by Orthodox Jews during the week of Passover—in memory of the hurried exodus from Egypt.
Mazzel-tov!	Hebrew for "Good luck!" The traditional form of congratulation on happy events.
Mes	Hebrew meaning "dead."
Mitzvah	Hebrew. Literally, a commandment. In popular use it came to mean a good deed, or ethical obligation.
M'sader K'dushin	Hebrew. A person qualified to perform the marriage ceremony.
Panninkeh	Polish-Yiddish. Affectionate diminutive for "my lord."
Purim	The Feast of Esther, celebrated in early spring on the day that Haman had chosen by casting lots ("purim") for the destruction of the Jews.
Rabban	Hebrew. Literally, "our teacher." The title, equivalent of chief rabbi, bestowed on certain presidents of the Sanhedrin.
Rashi	The popular designation formed from the initials of the title and name of *Rabbi Shelomo Itzhaki*.

GLOSSARY

Rav	A form of the title "Rabbi."
Reb	A courtesy title, equivalent to "Mister."
Rosh Ha-Shanah	Hebrew, literally "the head of the year." An important festival celebrated in autumn, the beginning of the "solemn days" or high holidays, and the opening of the Jewish religious year.
Shabbos	The divinely ordained day of rest. The Sabbath.
Shammas	Hebrew. The caretaker of a synagogue, usually assigned the duties of sexton, as well.
Shevorim	A broken, staccato cry sounded on the ram's horn.
Shlemihl	Yiddish. An awkward, inept person. A ne'er-do-well.
Shlimmazzel	Yiddish-Hebrew. A luckless person, for whom nothing goes well.
Simhah	Hebrew for "joy"; hence, a cause for rejoicing or festivity. A celebration.
Succoth	Hebrew for "booths." The Feast of Tabernacles, or booths. Celebrated in autumn to commemorate the wanderings in the wilderness.
Tallis	Hebrew. A prayer shawl, fringed at the corners or along the ends. Plural, tallesim.
Talmud	The mass of commentary and teachings on the Torah, or Mosaic Law, compiled in Babylon and also in Palestine, during several centuries.
T'kioh	The wailing sound of the ram's horn.
Torah	The five books of Moses (Genesis, Exodus, Leviticus, Numbers and Deuteronomy),

hand copied by scribes on parchment scrolls. In a broader sense, the Jewish teaching. A way of life.

T'ruoh   The trembling cry of the ram's horn.

Yeshiva   Hebrew. A Jewish school or academy, devoted chiefly to the study of the Talmud and rabbinic literature.